BRITISH MUSEUM (NA
ECONOMIC SERI

COMMON INSECT PESTS
OF STORED FOOD
PRODUCTS

A Guide to their Identification

BY
H. E. HINTON, Sc.D., Ph.D., F.R.S.

AND
A. STEVEN CORBET, D.Sc., Ph.D.

5th Edition

LONDON
TRUSTEES OF THE BRITISH MUSEUM
(NATURAL HISTORY)
1975

First edition 1943
New Impression 1944
Second edition 1949
Third edition with additions and amendments . . 1955
Fourth edition with further amendments . . . 1963
Fifth edition completely reset with amendments . . 1972
Reprinted 1975

ISBN 0 565 00565 0
Publication No. 565
BMNH/41.75/3m/8/75

Printed in England by Staples Printers Limited at The George Press, Kettering Northamptonshire

PREFACE TO THIRD EDITION

THE third edition of this work has been prepared by Dr. H. E. Hinton, now Reader in Entomology in the University of Bristol. Fifteen new illustrations have been added. Many additional species have been included, the selection of which has been partly based on the experience of the Infestation Control Division of the Ministry of Agriculture, generously placed at the disposal of the author.

N. D. RILEY,
Keeper

Department of Entomology,
British Museum (Natural History),
May, 1954

PREFACE TO FOURTH EDITION

THE fourth edition contains only a few minor changes needed to bring the nomenclature up to date and to clarify certain portions of the text.

J. P. DONCASTER,
Keeper

Department of Entomology,
British Museum (Natural History),
July, 1963

PREFACE TO FIFTH EDITION

THE fifth edition of this work by H. E. Hinton (now Professor of Zoology at the University of Bristol) and the late A. S. Corbet, is an interim measure, updated nomenclatorially by the staff of the Museum, but with a minimum of textual alteration.

PAUL FREEMAN,
Keeper

Department of Entomology,
British Museum (Natural History)
May, 1972

B

PREFACE TO THIRD EDITION

The third edition of this work has been prepared by Dr. J. F. Hinton, now Reader in Entomology in the University of Bristol. Fifteen new illustrations have been added. Many additional species have been included, the selection of which has been partly based on the experience of the Infestation Control Division of the Ministry of Agriculture, generously placed at the disposal of the author.

S. D. RILEY

Keeper

Department of Entomology,
British Museum (Natural History),
May, 1954.

PREFACE TO FOURTH EDITION

The fourth edition contains only a few minor changes needed to bring the nomenclature up to date and to clarify certain portions of the text.

J. P. DONCASTER

Keeper

Department of Entomology,
British Museum (Natural History),
July, 1962.

PREFACE TO FIFTH EDITION

The fifth edition of this work, by H. E. Hinton (now Professor of Zoology at the University of Bristol) and the late A. S. Corbet, in an interim measure, updated nomenclaturally by the staff of the Museum, but with a minimum of textual alteration.

PAUL FREEMAN

Keeper

Department of Entomology,
British Museum (Natural History)
May, 1975.

CONTENTS

		PAGE
INTRODUCTION	- - - - - - - - -	1
THYSANURA	- - - - - - - - - -	2
DICTYOPTERA	- - - - - - - - - -	3
ORTHOPTERA	- - - - - - - - - -	4
DERMAPTERA	- - - - - - - - - -	4
PSOCOPTERA	- - - - - - - - - -	5
HEMIPTERA	- - - - - - - - - -	6
COLEOPTERA	- - - - - - - - - -	8
LEPIDOPTERA	- - - - - - - - - -	42
HYMENOPTERA	- - - - - - - - - -	55
DIPTERA	- - - - - - - - - -	56
SIPHONAPTERA	- - - - - - - - - -	58
INDEX	- - - - - - - - - -	59

COMMON INSECT PESTS OF STORED FOOD PRODUCTS

A GUIDE TO THEIR IDENTIFICATION

INTRODUCTION

IN the following pages an attempt is made to make easy the identification of the insects commonly associated with stored food products in warehouses and granaries in this country.

The species are dealt with systematically Order by Order, and, following a brief general account of each Order, keys are given wherever necessary for the recognition of the families and species. The keys have been based mainly upon characters that can be seen in a good light with the use of a hand-lens ($\times 15$). This deliberate selection of the most easily observed characters has meant that in many instances no use could be made of taxonomically important characters since these often cannot be seen without the aid of a microscope.

Diagrams have been included to illustrate such structural characters as are used in the keys but are not easily defined in words. Some Orders, for instance the Psocoptera and Hymenoptera, are not dealt with in detail, as the identification of the species is too difficult for the layman. For the same reason keys have not been given to the species of some beetles, e.g. Bruchidae, *Cryptophagus* and *Cryptolestes*.*

---

* In case of difficulty, insects may be sent for identification to The Keeper, Department of Entomology, British Museum (Natural History), London, SW7 5BD, or to the local Public Health Inspector.

THYSANURA

The Order Thysanura includes about 200 primitive wingless insects with long, bristly, tail-like appendages. The antennae are long and many-segmented. The mouth-parts are adapted for biting. The abdomen is 11-segmented. There is no metamorphosis (external morphological changes undergone by young before reaching maturity), and the young closely resemble the adults.

Two species are commonly found, the "silver fish" or "silver

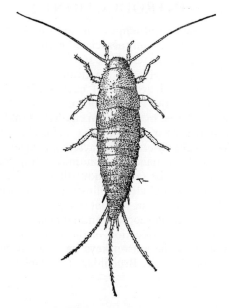

FIG. 1.—*Lepisma saccharina* Linnaeus. ×3½

moth" (*Lepisma saccharina* Linnaeus) and the "fire brat" (*Thermobia domestica* Packard). Both are about half an inch long when full grown. The silver fish can readily be recognised by reference to fig. 1. Its body is covered with silvery scales which give it a white, glistening appearance. The fire brat is similar in shape, but may be distinguished from the silver fish by the dark mottling on the dorsal surface of the body and the much longer antennae.

Both species are nocturnal and very active. They feed on a wide variety of starchy materials, and the silver fish is known to eat dead insects. They are general scavengers in the warehouse or granary.

DICTYOPTERA

This Order includes the cockroaches and mantids, two groups previously included in the Orthoptera. The antennae are long and many-segmented, and the mouth-parts are adapted for biting. The forewings (tegmina) are usually somewhat hardened and overlap along the mid-dorsal line. The hindwings are membranous, more

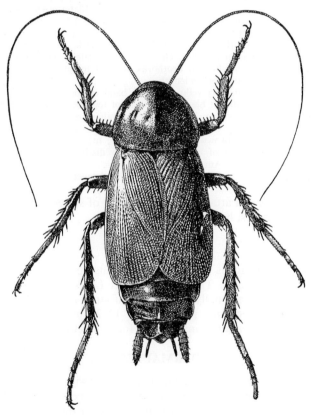

FIG. 2.—*Blatta orientalis* Linnaeus. ×2¾

delicate, and are folded under the tegmina. Both pairs of wings are sometimes much reduced in size or are even absent. The apex of the abdomen usually has segmented cerci of short or moderate length, and the female has only a short ovipositor. Metamorphosis is slight in winged species and wanting in wingless ones.

Four species of cockroaches occur in this country in buildings where food is available, but with the exception of *Blatta orientalis* Linnaeus they are rarely found in unheated buildings. The species may be distinguished as follows:

1. Dark brown, nearly black. Prothorax unicolorous. Adult male (fig. 2) with tegmina not extending to end of abdomen; adult female with tegmina lateral and lobe-like. 25 mm. "Oriental cockroach" or "black beetle" ....**Blatta orientalis** Linnaeus
    Reddish brown or dark yellow. Prothorax bicoloured. Adult males and females with tegmina extending to or beyond end of abdomen..........2
2. Dark yellow. Prothorax with two narrow, dark, longitudinal stripes. 12–14 mm. "German cockroach" ....**Blatella germanica** Linnaeus
    Reddish or chestnut-brown. Prothorax without longitudinal dark stripes. Adults 23 mm. or more in length 3
3. Prothorax with an ivory-yellow circular band enclosing a large, very distinct, bilobed, almost black spot. Base of tegmina with a narrow, submarginal, yellow stripe. 23–25 mm. "Australian cockroach"............
    ....**Periplaneta australasiae** Fabricius
    Prothorax reddish brown with a very large, median, somewhat diffused, darker spot. Base of tegmina without a distinct, yellow submarginal stripe. 29–35 mm. "American cockroach" ....
    ....**Periplaneta americana** Linnaeus

Cockroaches will attack almost any kind of stored food, and will also feed on boots, hair, and skins.

ORTHOPTERA

This Order includes such well-known insects as crickets, grasshoppers, and locusts. The house cricket (*Acheta domesticus* Linnaeus) (fig. 3) occasionally becomes a nuisance indoors. It is a very active, mainly nocturnal insect about 12–20 mm. long when full grown. It will eat almost any kind of food or refuse.

DERMAPTERA

The members of the Order Dermaptera (earwigs) are easily recognised because they have large forceps at the apex of the abdomen. The arms of the forceps are usually curved in the male and more or less straight in the female. In winged species the front pair of wings or tegmina are short and meet to form a straight mid-dorsal suture. The common earwig, *Forficula auricularia* Linnaeus (fig. 4), occasionally occurs indoors. It is 15–20 mm. long and dark brown. It feeds on a variety of substances, ranging from the tender foliage of plants to insects, living or dead. Two tropical species, *Euborellia annulipes* Lucas and *Marava arachidis* Yersin, are sometimes introduced with stored products. Both differ from the common earwig in having the second tarsal segment cylindrical instead of conspicuously dilated and produced beneath the third segment. *Marava* may be distinguished from *Euborellia* in that the fourth to

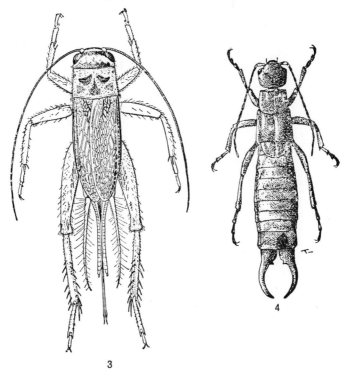

FIGS. 3–4.—(3) *Acheta domesticus* Linnaeus.   (4) *Forficula auricularia* Linnaeus.   ×2¾

sixth segments of the antennae are distinctly longer than instead of only about as long as the first segment. *Marava* also differs from *Euborellia* in lacking both tegmina and hindwings.

PSOCOPTERA

Psocids or book lice are small to minute, rather generalised insects. Some have two pairs of delicate, membranous wings and others are wingless or nearly so. The antennae are long, filiform, and have from 13 to about 50 segments. There are no cerci on the abdomen. Metamorphosis is slight or wanting.

c

Several pale grey or yellowish white wingless species about the size of a pinhead (fig. 5) are frequently found in very large numbers in warehouses and granaries, where they appear to be particularly attracted to the flour, meal, and other cereal products, especially if these are mouldy. Psocids will feed on a wide variety of plant and animal matter, e.g. fungi, lichens, paper, many kinds of stored food, dead insects, and so forth. They are sometimes found in large numbers among papers and books that have remained undisturbed for long periods; hence their name "book lice."

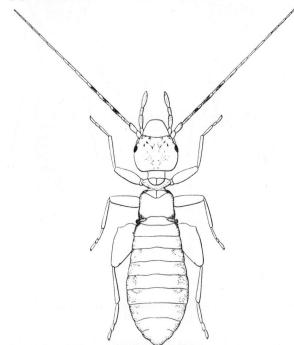

FIG. 5.—A psocid

HEMIPTERA

The Hemiptera or bugs are a large and very important Order of insects with some 50,000 described species, including such well-known species as bed bugs, white flies, scale insects, and plant lice. The species found associated with stored food products belong to the suborder Heteroptera, and they can be easily recognised by their peculiar head and wings. The head (fig. 6) always has a segmented rostrum or beak, which is usually long and slender and when not in use is held beneath the body with its apex directed backwards. The mouth-parts are always adapted for piercing and sucking, the mandibles and maxillae being modified to form slender, bristle-like stylets which are held in the grooved labium. Metamorphosis is gradual but distinct.

Two species, *Lyctocoris campestris* Fabricius and *Xylocoris* (*Arrostelus*) *flavipes* Reuter, commonly occur in warehouses and granaries, where they feed on the larvae of beetles and moths and on mites. *L. campestris* is 3·5–4 mm. long, the head, prothorax, and scutellum are dark brown to nearly black, and the forewings and legs are yellowish brown. *X. flavipes* (=*Piezostethus flavipes*) is

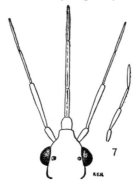

6

FIGS. 6–7.—(6) *Lyctocoris campestris* Fabricius with rostrum extended forwards
(7) Antenna of *Xylocoris flavipes* Reuter

similar in shape but smaller (2 mm. long), more reddish, and the adults are usually brachypterous (wings only partly developed in adult stage). Both nymphs and adults of *X. flavipes* may be distinguished by having the second and third segments of the antennae subequal in length (fig. 7), whereas in *L. campestris* the second is considerably longer than the third. *X. flavipes* has been recorded feeding on the larvae of *Ephestia*, *Plodia*, *Oryzaephilus* and *Tribolium*.

Two other bugs are much more rarely found in buildings in this country: *Reduvius personatus* Linnaeus, which is about 16–17 mm. long when adult, and *Peregrinator biannulipes* Montrouzier, which is 6–7 mm. In *R. personatus* the second and third antennal segments are nearly equal, whereas in *P. biannulipes* the third segment is nearly twice as long as the second.

Amphibolus venator Klug is a frequent arrival in this country with African groundnuts. It is dark brown, 9–10 mm. long, and may most readily be distinguished from the preceding two species by its size.

COLEOPTERA*

Beetles comprise the largest natural Order in the animal kingdom, and there are already probably no less than 250,000 described species. More than 600 of these have been found associated with stored food products at one time or another in various parts of the world, and among them are most of the major pests. Many of the species that are able to maintain themselves in houses, warehouses, and granaries do no direct damage to grain or other kinds of stored food, but feed only on refuse or on fungi, and a few are predacious and therefore beneficial.

Adult beetles may be distinguished by having horny or leathery forewings (elytra) which meet to form a straight mid-dorsal suture.

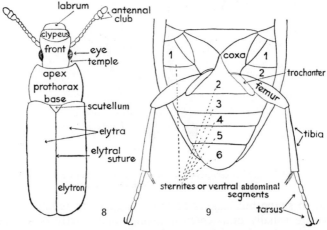

FIGS. 8–9.—(8) Dorsal view of a beetle. (9) Ventral abdominal view of a Carabid beetle. Diagrammatic

and membranous hindwings which are folded beneath the elytra. The hindwings of both sexes are sometimes very much reduced and represented only by scale-like stumps, e.g. in *Sitophilus granarius* Linnaeus. Like other insects with a complete metamorphosis, beetles have four distinct stages in their life-cycle, egg→larva→pupa→adult.

The larvae of the beetles found associated with stored food products may be distinguished from those of all other insects found in similar situations by possessing the following combination of characters: head distinct and generally darker in colour than

---

* For a more detailed account of many of the species see Hinton, H. E. 1945, *A monograph of the beetles associated with stored products*. Vol. I British Museum (Natural History), viii + 443 pp., 505 figs.

remainder of body, with well-developed biting mouth-parts and without compound eyes but usually with 1–6 simple eyes or ocelli on each side; thorax with three pairs of legs; and abdomen without paired pseudopods. A few, e.g. weevils, have no thoracic legs but are otherwise similar. Weevil larvae are short and very stout and the mandibles bite horizontally, whereas the legless larvae of those Diptera that are found in stored products and have a distinct head, are long and narrow, and the mandibles bite vertically.

Since the conspicuous characters selected for use in the keys which follow are not necessarily of primary taxonomic importance, members of a single family may be found to occur in more than one section of the main key. Where two or more species of a family are dealt with, a separate key will be found under the heading of the family; and in practice this will mean that as soon as a family can be recognised at sight the reader need only use the key to the species of that family.

The more important distinguishing features of the families that are dealt with separately are briefly summarised, but when using these summaries it should be remembered that exceptions to the general rule are dealt with only if they concern the warehouse or granary inspector. The principal character given for the Nitidulidae, for example, is the exposed two or three apical segments of the abdomen, but this is only true of those species dealt with here, the majority of this family having fewer exposed dorsal abdominal segments. To use the keys it is necessary to know the names of the parts of the body shown in figs. 8–9.

Key to adult beetles

1. Head strongly produced in front of eyes to form a narrow snout or beak (figs. 25–27). "Weevils"......................**Curculionidae** p. 19
   Head without a distinct snout...2
2. Prothorax (fig. 13) with a short, narrow apical neck so that head is completely exposed and is never even partly received into anterior part of prothorax. 3·0–3·5 mm....................**Anthicus** spp. (Anthicidae)
   Prothorax without an apical neck and head always with at least base fitting into prothorax...3
3. Elytra always leaving at least one dorsal abdominal segment exposed......4
   Elytra completely covering all dorsal abdominal segments*..........10
4. Elytra very short. Abdomen flexible, with at least six ventral segments and usually with six or more exposed dorsal segments (fig. 17). 0·5–15 mm. (Black or brown, long and narrow, active beetles of little importance in stored products.) ....**Staphylinidae**
   Elytra moderately long. Abdomen hard and not flexible, with not more than five ventral segments, and never with more than three exposed dorsal segments 5

---

* It should be noted that in some specimens the abdomen may be unnaturally extended at death.

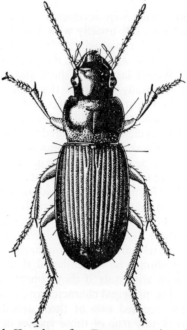

FIG. 10.—A Carabid, *Harpalus rufipes* Degeer, sometimes found in warehouses and granaries.   ×4.   (After Hinton, 1945)

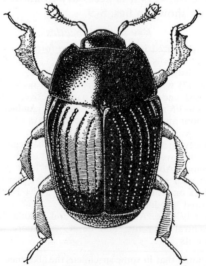

FIG. 11.—*Carcinops pumilio* Erichson.   ×11.   (After Hinton, 1945)

5. Funicle of antenna (i.e. segments between first and apical club) forming
a distinct angle with the first segment so that the antenna appears to
be elbowed (fig. 11). Head below and in front of the eye with a groove
that receives the first antennal segment when the latter is retracted.
Body broadly oval and cuticle strongly shining and black. Length
usually 1·5–4·0 mm., occasionally as much as 9 mm.......**Histeridae***
Antenna not elbowed and head without grooves for the reception of the
first antennal segment..6

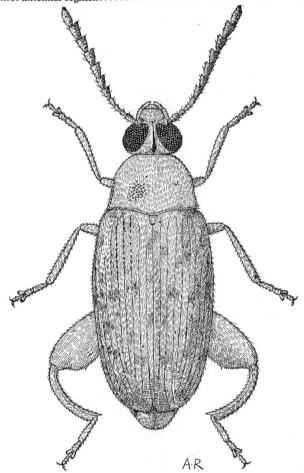

FIG. 12.—*Caryedon serratus* Olivier.   ×*c.* 13

---

* The Histeridae associated with stored products are described in detail
by Hinton, H. E., 1945, *Bull ent. Res.* **35:** 309–340, 56 figs. *Carcinops pumilio*
Erichson (fig. 11) is the commonest histerid found in stored products.

6. Antenna 10-segmented; club large and 1-segmented. Narrow species 1·8–2·5 mm. long .... **Monotoma** spp. (Rhizophagidae)
   Antenna 11-segmented; club of more than one segment or without a distinct club. Species broader and usually longer........................7
7. Antenna with a large, distinct, compact, 3-segmented club. Abdomen (fig. 28) with two or three exposed dorsal segments. Elytra not striate .... **Nitidulidae**, p. 21

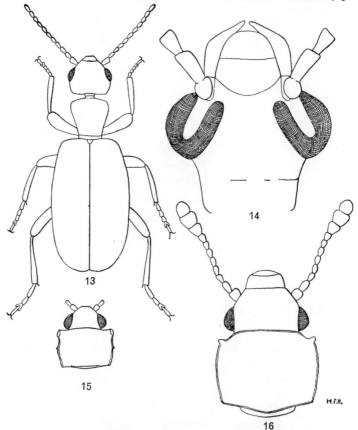

FIGS. 13–16.—(13) *Anthicus floralis* Linnaeus.   ×19. (14) *Bruchus* sp. (15) *Cryptophagus cellaris* Scopoli.   (16) *Ahasverus advena* Waltl

Antenna either not clubbed or if with a club the latter is never large, compact, and 3-segmented. Abdomen with only the last dorsal segment exposed, this segment, the pygidium, usually almost vertically inclined. Elytra deeply striate 8
8. Antenna with three apical segments distinctly larger than other segments. Eyes entire, nowhere emarginate. 3·0–4·5 mm. long. "Coffee-bean weevil" ....**Araecerus fasciculatus** Degeer (Anthribidae)

Antenna with three apical segments not distinctly larger than all other segments (fig. 12) 9
9. Each eye (fig. 14) with a broad and deep emargination which extends backwards from the base of the antenna. Species usually not over 5 mm· long. "Bean weevils" or "pea weevils"................................
...............................**Bruchidae*** (*Bruchus, Callosobruchus*)
Eye (fig. 12) without a deep emargination. Species usually over 5 mm. long ....**Bruchidae** (*Caryedon*)
10. First ventral segment of abdomen completely divided by hind coxae (fig. 9). (Very active beetles usually more than half an inch long; black or nearly black and often with a strong metallic lustre; antennae filiform, not clubbed, 11-segmented; all tarsi 5-segmented. Rare in granaries and warehouses.) ....**Carabidae** (fig. 10)
First ventral segment of abdomen not divided but extending in one piece from side to side 11

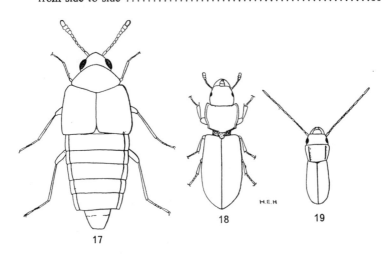

17

18   19

Figs. 17–19.—(17) *Oligota granaria* Erichson. ×45. (18) *Tenebroides mauritanicus* Linnaeus. ×*c*. 10. (19) *Cryptolestes* sp. ×5

11. Elytra with a blue or blue-green metallic lustre on at least apical half ....**Cleridae** p. 30
12. Elytra never blue or blue-green 12
Species about an inch (20–24 mm.) long. Black. Front and middle tarsi 5-segmented, hind tarsi 4-segmented. "Churchyard beetle" ....
....**Blaps mucronata** Latreille (Tenebrionidae), p. 37
Species never more than 18 mm. long 13
13. Species 14–18 mm. long and brown or black. Front and middle tarsi 5-segmented, hind tarsi 4-segmented ....
..............................**Tenebrionidae** (*Tenebrio*), p. 36
Species 11 mm. or less 14

* Keys to the Bruchidae of economic importance have been given by Herford, G. M., 1935, *Trans Soc. Brit. E· t*. **2** : 1–32.

14. Prothorax with six (fig. 29) or more (fig. 20) teeth on each side.........15
    Prothorax with not more than two large teeth on each side, or without
    teeth; disk of prothorax never with three longitudinal ridges 16
15. Prothorax (fig. 29) with six large teeth on each side; disk of prothorax
    with three longitudinal ridges. 2·5–3·5 mm. (Dark brown, rather flat.)
    ....**Silvanidae** (*Oryzaephilus*), p. 22
    Prothorax with more than six, usually nine or ten, small and more or less
    equal teeth on each side; disk of prothorax without longitudinal ridges
    (fig. 20). 1·7–2·1 mm. (Pale brown, moderately hairy. Antenna with
    a 3-segmented club.) ....
    ....**Henoticus californicus** Mannerheim (Cryptophagidae)

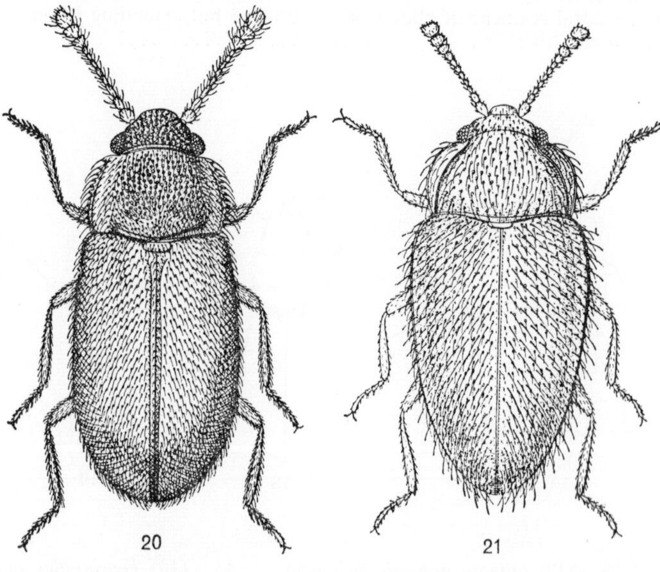

FIGS. 20–21.—(20) *Henoticus californicus* Mannerheim. ×27. (21) *Mycetaea hirta*
Marsham.   ×32.   (After Hinton, 1945)

16. Prothorax with an entire sublateral ridge or carina on each side more or
    less parallel with and near to lateral margin (figs. 19 and 21) 17
    Prothorax without sublateral ridges 18
17. Antennae usually more than half as long as body and without an apical
    club (fig. 19). Body very flat. 1·3–5·0 mm. ....
    ....**Cryptolestes, Leptophloeus,** and **Planolestes** spp. (Cucujidae)*
    Antennae much less than half as long as body and with a distinct 2-seg-
    mented apical club. Body strongly convex and hairy (fig. 21). 1·5–1·8 mm.
    ....**Mycetaea hirta** Marsham (Endomychidae)

* The European Laemophloeinae, including those from stored products, are
keyed by Lefkovitch, L. P., 1959, *Trans R. ent. Soc. Lond.*, **111** : 95–118.

18. Prothorax very densely and, particularly anteriorly, coarsely tuberculate (fig. 22). 2·5–3·0 mm. (Cylindrical and brown; head deflexed and more or less concealed from above by prothorax; antennae with a large, loose, 3-segmented club.) "Lesser grain borer"..................
.... **Rhizopertha dominica** Fabricius (Bostrichidae)
Prothorax punctate, occasionally also with a few very fine tubercles......19

19. Prothorax with apical angles distinctly toothed or with a very much thickened (figs. 15–16), nearly smooth, oval, disk-like area. (Less than 4 mm., usually pale brown, moderately densely hairy, and with a 2- or 3-segmented antennal club.).......................................20
Prothorax with apical angles not toothed or thickened................21

20. Prothorax (fig. 15) with a distinct tooth on about middle of lateral margin. 1·5–3·5 mm.....................**Cryptophagus** spp. (Cryptophagidae)
Prothorax (fig. 16) without a tooth on middle of lateral margin. 2–3 mm.
........................**Ahasverus advena** Waltl (Silvanidae), p. 22

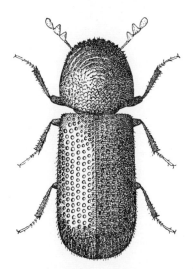

Fig. 22.—*Rhizopertha dominica* Fabricius. ×22

21. Antennae not thickened apically (apical three segments never broader than second segment), without a club, usually more than half as long as body, 11-segmented. Prothorax constricted at base and this basal region usually on a much lower plane than middle of disk so that prothorax has a distinct neck. All tarsi 5-segmented. 1·8–4·5 mm. (Brown or golden-brown rather hairy beetles which, because of their oval bodies and long legs, resemble small spiders, figs. 54–59.) ....**Ptinidae, p. 34**
Antennae with apical segments always thicker than second segment and often forming a distinct club, less than half as long as body. Prothorax usually without a basal neck-like constriction, but if such is present the antennae are clubbed...22

22. Prothorax with a short and narrow but very distinct basal neck narrower than in fig. 48, 5·0–6·5 mm. (Elongate, subparallel, brown beetles with sparse and erect hairs on dorsal surface, a 3-segmented antennal club, and tarsi all 5-segmented.).......... **Thaneroclerus buqueti** Lefèvre (Cleridae), p. 31
Prothorax without a distinct basal neck............................23

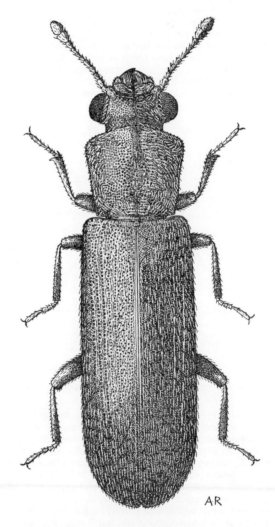

AR

Fig. 23.—*Lyctus brunneus* Stephens.   ×25

23. Antennae with a large, compact, very distinct, 2-segmented club (fig. 23),
2·2–7 mm. long. (Narrow, parallel, brown beetles similar in appearance to
Tribolium but differing in having all tarsi instead of only the hind tarsi
4-segmented and the antennal club with two instead of with three or
more segments.) "The brown powder post beetle"....................
...................**Lyctus brunneus** Stephens (Bostrichidae—Lyctinae)
Antennae with club of three or more segments (except some species of
Anthrenus, but the latter are very convex, nearly round beetles covered
with white and brown or black scales) or without a distinct club......24
24. Antennae received in large cavities visible on a frontal view in the front
of the prothorax (fig. 37). Body strongly convex, nearly round, and
dorsal surface conspicuously clothed with alternating patches of white
and blackish or brownish scales. 2–4 mm. long.....................
....**Dermestidae** (*Anthrenus*), p. 27

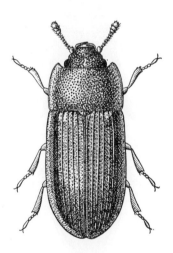

Fig. 24.—*Lophocateres pusillus* Klug. ×17

Antennae not received in cavities in the front of the prothorax (from a
frontal view no cavities can be seen). Body oblong-oval to parallel and
never with scales though sometimes (e.g. *Dermestes*, figs. 43–44) with
black and white hairs 25
25. Dorsal surface without hairs or at most with a few very short, microscopic
hairs not visible with a hand-lens 26
Dorsal surface distinctly hairy (hairs always distinct—×15 mag.—if specimen is viewed laterally against the light)........................29
26. Distinctly flattened species. All tarsi 5-segmented, but basal segment is
so small that all tarsi appear to be 4-segmented when seen with a hand
lens 27
Distinctly convex species. All tarsi 3-segmented or with tarsi of front and
middle legs 5-segmented and those of hind legs 4-segmented.........28

27. Prothorax with base distinctly separated from base of elytra (fig. 18).
    Elytra without longitudinal ridges. 5–11 mm. "Cadelle" ....
    ....**Tenebroides mauritanicus** Linnaeus (Trogositidae)
    Prothorax with base closely applied to base of elytra. Elytra with distinct
    longitudinal ridges (fig. 24). 2·7–3·2 mm. "Siamese grain beetle"
    ....**Lophocateres pusillus** Klug (Lophocateridae)

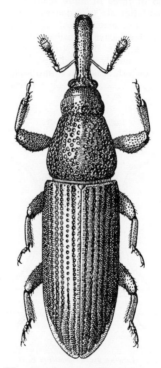

FIG. 25.—*Euophryum confine* Broun.   ×24

28. Antennal club 2- or 3-segmented. Tarsi all 3-segmented. 1·2–3·0 mm.
    (figs. 30–33)...................................**Lathridiidae,** p. 23
    Antennae not distinctly clubbed or with club more than 3-segmented
    (except *Tribolium castaneum* which has a 3-segmented club, but is parallel-
    sided instead of obovate, has the eyes distinctly divided by the side
    margins of head, the prothorax not explanate or depressed, and is 3–4
    mm. long). Prothorax with sides never explanate and disk evenly convex
    from side to side. Front and middle tarsi 5-segmented and hind tarsi
    4-segmented. ....**Tenebrionidae,** p. 37
29. Basal half of elytra (fig. 42) grey or pale brown with three large black spots
    on each elytron in middle of pale area; apical half black. 7–9 mm. long.
    ....**Dermestes lardarius** Linnaeus (Dermestidae), p. 28
    Elytra usually unicolorous, if maculate never as above................30

Coleoptera 19

30. Sides of prothorax entirely clothed with dense white hairs (fig. 44). Most
of ventral surface densely clothed with white hairs and with only a few
lateral patches of black hairs. 5·5–10 mm.........................
.............................Dermestidae (*Dermestes* spp.), p. 27
Sides of prothorax without or with only very few white hairs. Ventral
surface with ashy, golden, or golden and brown hairs forming a pattern. .31
31. Species 7–9 mm. long (fig. 43) 32
Species 5·5 mm. long or less 33
32. Ventral surface of abdomen clearly patterned with dark patches on a golden
ground colour. First abdominal segment with lateral impressed lines
strongly curved inward at base, meeting hind coxae away from outer
edge. 7–9 mm. long (fig. 43).......................................
........................Dermestes ater Degeer (Dermestidae) p. 30
Ventral surface of abdomen more or less evenly clothed with golden hairs.
First abdominal segment with lateral impressed lines not curved inward
toward base, ending opposite lateral margin of hind coxae. 7–9 mm. long.
.................Dermestes peruvianus Castelnau (Dermestidae) p. 30
..............Dermestes haemorrhoidalis Küster (Dermestidae) p. 30
33. Elytra black with two small oval spots of white hairs on middle (fig. 46)
4–5·5 mm. (Head with a median ocellus).........................
....................Attagenus pellio Linnaeus (Dermestidae), p. 30
Elytra not as above..34
34. Head with a median ocellus (fig. 36). Elytra never striate................
....Dermestidae, p. 27
Head without a median ocellus. Elytra usually striate.................35
35. Antennal club 4-segmented. Prothorax with a distinct oval pit on each
side near base. Each elytron (fig. 34) with a large basal and a smaller
subapical pale brown spot. 3·5–4·0 mm. (Elytra distinctly striate. Tarsi
all 4-segmented except front tarsi of male, which are 3-segmented.)
...........................Mycetophagidae (*Mycetophagus*), p. 26
Antennal club 3-segmented or 8-segmented. Prothorax without basal pits.
Elytra unicolorous...36
36. Antennal club 3-segmented, compact, and distinctly shorter than remainder of antenna. Tarsi all 4-segmented except front tarsi of male,
which are 3-segmented. 2·5–3·0 mm. (General appearance, fig. 35, almost
identical to *Cryptophagus* but without the prothoracic teeth of the latter.)
................................Mycetophagidae (*Typhaea*), p. 27
Antennal club 3- or 8-segmented and always much longer than remainder
of antenna. Tarsi all 5-segmented. (Small brown beetles with head usually
held under prothorax so that it is not visible from above).............
....Anobiidae, p. 32

CURCULIONIDAE

The Curculionidae or true weevils form the largest family in the
animal kingdom. There are about 40,000 described species. They
attack twigs, bark, roots, leaves, and buds. Many species feed on
seeds and nuts. About 30 species have been recorded in stored food
products in various parts of the world, and of these four are
commonly found in this country. From all other beetles dealt with

here they may be distinguished by having the head produced in front of the eyes to form a well-defined snout, the antennae elbowed and clubbed, and all tarsi 4-segmented. The larvae have no legs, are stout and slightly curved, and are white with a pale brown or yellowish head.

1. Elytra short, so that the apical dorsal abdominal segment is visible from above. Antenna 8-segmented....................................2
   Elytra completely covering the apical dorsal abdominal segment. Antenna 7- or 9-segmented 3
2. Prothorax with punctures distinctly oblong or oblong-oval. Elytra with intervals much broader than striae or strial punctures. Hindwings absent. 3–4 mm. "Granary or grain weevil" ....
   ....(*Calandra granaria* =) **Sitophilus granarius** Linnaeus
   Prothorax very densely set with round or irregularly shaped punctures. Elytra with intervals usually distinctly narrower than striae or strial punctures; elytra usually with four reddish spots. Hindwings always present. 2·3–4·5 mm. "Rice and Maize weevils" ....
   (*Calandra oryzae* =) **Sitophilus zeamais** Motschulsky, **S. oryzae** Linnaeus*
3. Antennae 9-segmented (fig. 26). 2·5–3·5 mm. (This species is common in grain in southern United States. The absence of British records may be due to its close superficial resemblance to the species of *Sitophilus*) "Broad-nosed grain weevil" ....
   ...... (*Caulophilus latinasus* auctt. =) **Caulophilus oryzae** Gyllenhal
   Antennae 7-segmented 4

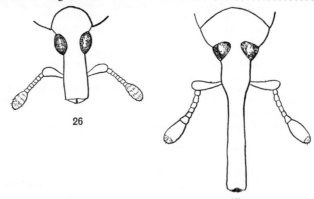

26

27

FIGS. 26–27.—(26) Head of *Caulophilus oryzae* Gyllenhal. (27) Head of *Sitophilus oryzae* Linnaeus

4. Elytra with apical sides dilated and distinctly flexed upwards (fig. 25). Head narrowly and deeply constricted immediately behind the eyes. 2·8–4·8 mm. ....**Euophryum confine** Broun
   Elytra with apical sides not flexed upwards. Head only slightly constricted behind eyes ....**Pentarthrum huttoni** Wollaston

---

* The two species, found in similar situations, although seldom together, are almost indistinguishable on external characters.

NITIDULIDAE

More than 2,000 species of Nitidulidae, or "sap-feeding beetles," have been described. Many feed on the sap of trees and juice of fruits, especially when partly fermented. Many live on flowers, fungi, and carrion, whereas a few are predacious and a few are leaf miners. About 16 species have been recorded on stored food products or in warehouses and granaries. Of these, three commonly occur in similar situations in this country. They are obovate or oblong beetles having an 11-segmented antenna with a compact 3-segmented club. The elytra are somewhat shortened so that two or three apical abdominal segments are exposed from above. The abdomen always has five visible ventral segments, but in the males a small sixth segment is sometimes visible. The tarsi are all 5-segmented, and the fourth segment is always shorter than the others.

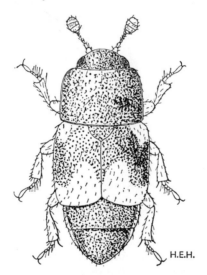

H.E.H.

FIG. 28.—*Carpophilus hemipterus* Linnaeus. ×19

1. Each elytron dark brown with a large and distinct pale (usually yellow) spot at apex and a smaller spot at base (fig. 28). 2–4 mm. "Dried-fruit beetle" . . . . **Carphophilus hemipterus** Linnaeus
   Elytra unicolorous or with sutural region slightly darker than rest of elytra 2
2. Mesosternal disk with a median longitudinal carina. 2·3–4·5 mm. . . . .
   . . . . **Carpophilus obsoletus** Erichson
   Mesosternal disk without longitudinal carinae and more or less evenly convex 3

3. Disk of prothorax and elytra distinctly convex; base of prothorax as broad
   as base of elytra and sides not sinuate before the broadly rounded basal
   angles. 2·0–3·5 mm. ....**Carpophilus "dimidiatus Group"***
   Disk of prothorax and elytra distinctly flattened; base of prothorax narrower
   than base of elytra and sides feebly sinuate before the nearly acute hind
   angles. 2·8–4·0 mm. ....**Carpophilus ligneus** Murray

SILVANIDAE

The Silvanidae are a small family closely related to the Cucujidae
(*Cryptolestes*, etc.). They are usually narrow and distinctly flattened
and have 11-segmented antennae with a compact club. The elytra
completely cover the abdomen, and there are only five visible ventral

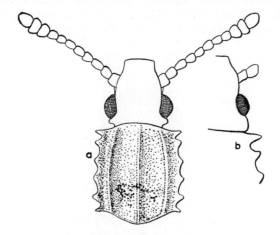

FIG. 29.—(a) *Oryzaephilus mercator* Fauvel.   (b) *O. surinamensis* Linnaeus

abdominal segments. The tarsi are all 5-segmented. Most of the
species are probably predacious, but about 15 have been recorded
in stored food products in various parts of the world. Of these, three
are commonly found in this country, one of them, *Ahasverus advena*,
probably feeding only on moulds and refuse.

1. Prothorax (fig. 16) with a single large tooth on each apical angle; sides
   not toothed; disk evenly convex. 2–3 mm. "Foreign grain beetle"
   ....(*Catharus advena* =) **Ahasverus advena** Waltl
   Prothorax (fig. 29) with six large teeth on each side; disk with three low
   longitudinal ridges 2

* Several species, all associated with stored products and very closely related
one to another, key out at this point.

2. Head with length of temple (region directly behind eye) equal to more
than half of vertical diameter of eye (fig. 29b). 2·5–3·5 mm. "Saw-toothed
grain beetle" . . . .
. . . . *(Silvanus surinamensis=)* **Oryzaephilus surinamensis** Linnaeus
Head with length of temple much less than half of vertical diameter of eye
(fig. 29a) 2·5–3·5 mm. "Merchant grain beetle" . . . .
. . . . *(Silvanus mercator =)* **Oryzaephilus mercator** Fauvel

LATHRIDIIDAE*

The Lathridiidae are a small family of beetles 1–3 mm. long,
usually obovate, and pale brown to nearly black. The antennae of the
species dealt with here are 11-segmented with a rather compact 2- or
3-segmented club; the sides of the prothorax are somewhat explanate
(dilated), and the surface is depressed along the middle and trans-
versely near the base. The elytra completely cover the abdomen,
and there are five ventral abdominal segments. All tarsi are
3-segmented. The adults and larvae feed on fungi, particularly
moulds, and do not attack stored foods. About 35 species have
been found in warehouses, granaries, etc., in various parts of the
world. Several of these are common in this country, but as their
specific differentiation is rather difficult, a key is given only to the
seven most common species.

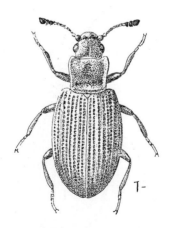

Fig. 30.—*Lathridius minutus* Linnaeus. ×24

---

* For a full account of all the species of economic importance, see Hinton
H. E., 1941, "The Lathridiidae of Economic Importance," *Bull. Ent. Res.*, **32**
191–247, 67 figs.

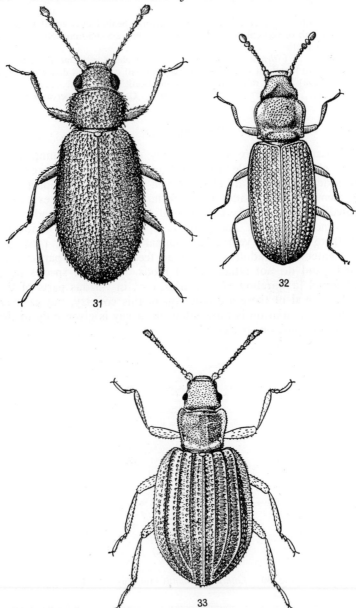

FIGS. 31–33.—(31) *Corticaria pubescens* Gyllenhal.   ×22.   (32) *Microgramme filiformis* Gyllenhal.   ×40.   (33) *Thes bergrothi* Reitter.   ×28. (After Hinton, 1941)

1. Clypeus on same plane as front of head. Elytra never with ridged or carinate intervals; striae not deeply impressed; surface distinctly hairy (fig. 31). 2·3–3·0 mm. .... **Corticaria pubescens** Gyllenhal*
Clypeus on a slightly lower plane than front of head. Elytra with the intervals often ridged or carinate; striae always well marked and often deeply impressed; surface without hairs or only indistinctly hairy 2

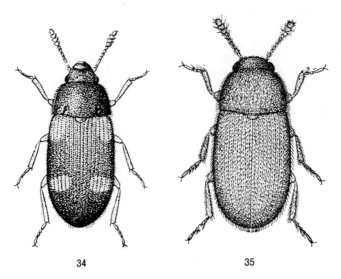

34   35

FIGS. 34–35.—(34) *Mycetophagus quadriguttatus* Müller. ×12. (35) *Typhaea stercorea* Linnaeus. ×15. (After Hinton, 1945)

2. Prothorax with a feeble or distinct ridge on each side of middle. Each elytron with intervals 3, 5, and 7 (counting from suture outwards) sharply ridged (fig. 33) 3
Prothorax without longitudinal ridges. Each elytron with all intervals flat or at most feebly convex 5
3. Pronotum not strongly constricted at basal third, each side at most only moderately sinuate at basal third (fig. 33). Tarsi with first segment distinctly shorter than second. 1·8–2·2 mm. ....
.... **Thes bergrothi** Reitter
Pronotum strongly constricted at basal third. Tarsi with two basal segments nearly equal in length 4
4. Antennal club 3-segmented. Elytra with broad and transverse depressions; each elytron with a very large and longitudinal swelling on the apical third of the third interval. Male with a large tooth near inner apex of hind tibia. 1·5–2·1 mm. ....**Aridius nodifer** Westwood

---

* *C. punctulata* Marsham, an extremely closely related species, also keys out at this point.

Antennal club 2-segmented. Elytra without transverse depressions; each elytron without a swelling on third interval. Male without a tooth on inner apex of hind tibia. 1·2–1·7 mm. ....
.... **Cartodere constrictus** Gyllenhal
5. Eyes large, separated by less than their diameter from the base of the antennae. Scutellum distinct and horizontal. Prothorax everywhere much narrower than base of elytra (fig. 30). 1·2–2·4 mm. ....
.... **Lathridius "minutus Group"***
  Eyes small, separated by one to two diameters from base of antennae. Scutellum indistinct from above and usually more or less vertical. Prothorax anteriorly as broad as base of elytra (fig. 32) 6
6. Antenna with club 2-segmented. 1·2–1·6 mm. ....**Microgramme filum** Aubé
  Antenna with club 3-segmented (fig. 32). 1·2–1·4 mm. ....
.... **Microgramme filiformis** Gyllenhal

M<small>YCETOPHAGIDAE</small>

The Mycetophagidae include about 200 species of small (1·5–5·0 mm. long), oblong to oval, moderately depressed, usually densely

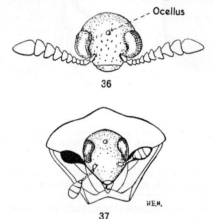

F<small>IGS</small>. 36–37.—(36) Head of *Trogoderma inclusum* Le Conte. (37) Front view of head and prothorax of *Anthrenus scrophulariae* Linnaeus

pubescent beetles which are brown or black and generally have yellow or reddish spots on the elytra. The antennae are 11-segmented with a 2- to 5-segmented club. The elytra completely cover the abdomen, and there are five ventral abdominal segments. All tarsi are 4-segmented except the front tarsi of the males which are 3-segmented. The larvae and adults of nearly all species, including

---

* Three extremely similar species key out here, *Lathridius minutus, L. pseudominutus* and *L. anthracinus*.

those associated with stored food products, feed on fungi. Five species have been found on stored food products, and of these two occur in this country.

1. Antennal club 4-segmented. Prothorax with a distinct oval pit on each side near base. Elytra distinctly striate; each elytron with a large basal and a small subapical brown spot (fig. 34). 3·5- 4·0 mm. . . . .
. . . .**Mycetophagus quadriguttatus** Muller
   Antennal club 3-segmented. Prothorax without basal pits. Elytra unicolorous and not striate but with hairs arranged in longitudinal rows (fig. 35) so that they look striate. 2·5–3·0 mm. "Hairy fungus beetle"
. . . .(*T. fumata* =) **Typhaea stercorea** Linnaeus

DERMESTIDAE

About 600 species of Dermestidae are known. They are small to moderately large beetles densely covered with hairs or scales which are often conspicuously coloured. The head is small, somewhat deflexed, and usually bears a median ocellus. The antennae are 5- to 11-segmented, short, and with a distinct and often relatively large club. The elytra completely cover the abdomen, and there are five visible ventral abdominal segments. All tarsi are 5-segmented. These beetles feed on all kinds of dried animal matter, particularly skins, furs, woollens, dried fish, etc., and a number will attack dried vegetable products. About 55 species have been reported as injurious. The key given below includes all the more important species found in Britain. The species of *Anthrenus* are not dealt with in detail, as they cannot be distinguished easily with a hand-lens.

1. Head without a median ocellus. Species 5·5–10·0 mm. long 2
   Head with a median ocellus (fig. 36). Species 1·5–5·5 mm. long. 7
2. Each side of pronotum (fig. 44) with a broad band of white or yellowish white hairs. Sternum of metathorax and abdomen white with a few patches of black hairs at sides. Lateral impressed line of first abdominal sternite broad and not extending to hind margin of segment 3
   Pronotum entirely black or also with brownish hairs, but never with a distinct lateral band of whitish hairs. Sternum of metathorax and abdomen more or less uniformly black or brownish. Lateral impressed line of first abdominal sternite extending to hind margin of segment 5
3. Each elytron with inner apex (fig. 38) produced behind to form an acute spine. 5·5–10 mm. "Hide or leather beetle" . . . .
. . . .(*D. vulpinus* F. =) **Dermestes maculatus** Degeer
   Each elytron rounded at apex (fig. 39). 4
4. Fifth ventral segment of abdomen with a patch of black hairs on apex and one on each side at base (fig. 41); lateral impressed lines present only on anterior part of first segment. Male with a median brush of hairs (fig. 41) present only on fourth abdominal sternite. 6–9 mm. . . . .
. . . .**Dermestes frischii** Kugelann

Fifth ventral segment of abdomen without an apical patch of black hairs (fig. 40); lateral impressed lines always present on first, third, fourth, and fifth segments. Male (fig. 40) with a median brush of hairs present on third and fourth abdominal sternites. 6·5–8·5 mm. . . . .
. . . .**Dermestes carnivorus** Fabricius
5. Basal half of each elytron with pale brown hairs in the middle of which are three small patches of black hairs (fig. 42); apical half of elytra black. Abdomen with lateral impressed line of first ventral segment not strongly curved inwards at base and ending some distance from hind coxa. 7–9 mm. "Larder beetle" . . . .**Dermestes lardarius** Linnaeus

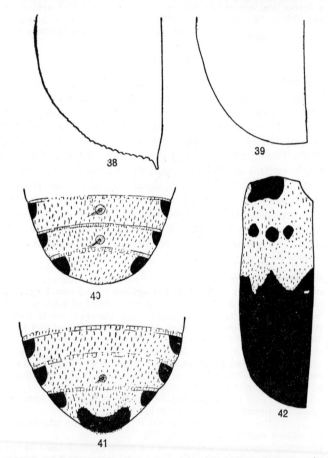

Figs. 38–42.—(38) Apex of elytron of *Dermestes maculatus* Degeer. (39) Same of *D. frischii* Kugelann. (40) Apex of ventral side of abdomen of male of *D. carnivorus* Fabricius. (41) Same of *D. frischii* Kugelann. (42) Elytron of *D. lardarius* Linnaeus.

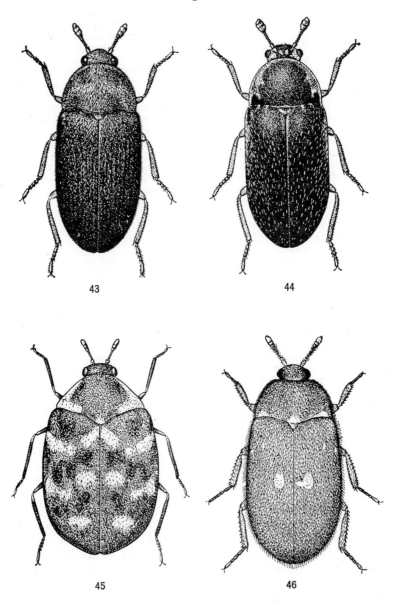

43

44

45

46

FIGS. 43–46.—(43) *Dermestes ater* Degeer. ×7. (44) *Dermestes frischii* Kugelann. ×7. (45) *Anthrenus verbasci* Linnaeus. ×16. (46) *Attagenus pellio* Linnaeus. ×10. (After Hinton, 1945)

Elytra uniformly clothed, basal half not paler than apical half (fig. 43).
Abdomen with lateral impressed line of first ventral segment variable. ...6
6. Ventral surface of abdomen clearly patterned with dark patches on a golden
ground colour. First abdominal segment with lateral impressed lines
strongly curved inward at base, meeting hind coxae away from their
outer edge. 7–9 mm. long. (fig 43). ....**Dermestes ater** Degeer
Ventral surface of abdomen more or less evenly clothed with golden hairs.
First abdominal segment with lateral impressed lines not curved inward
toward base, ending opposite lateral margins of hind coxae. 7–9 mm. long.
..................................**Dermestes peruvianus** Castelnau
..........................**Dermestes haemorrhoidalis** Küster
7. Antennae received in large cavities in the front of the prothorax (fig. 37).
Body (fig. 45) strongly convex, nearly round, 2–4 mm. long, and dorsal
surface conspicuously clothed with alternating patches of white and
blackish or brownish scales. Legs short; when retracted they are received
into more or less distinct grooves on the ventral surface ....
....**Anthrenus** spp.
Prothorax without cavities for the reception of the antennae or, if cavities
are present, they are not visible from a frontal view. Body oblong and
without scales 8
8. Elytra with two small median patches of white hairs or, if unicolorous,
3·3–5·0 mm. long. Antennal club 3-segmented. First segment of tarsi
half as long as second 9
Elytra with numerous irregular patches of pale hairs, but if unicolorous
3·0 mm. long or less. Antennal club at least 4-segmented. First segment
of tarsus much longer than second 10
9. Elytra (fig. 46) black except for a small patch of white hairs on either side
near middle. Base of prothorax at middle and side clothed with white
hairs. 4·5–5·0 mm. ....**Attagenus pellio** Linnaeus
Elytra entirely black or brown. Prothorax without distinct white hairs.
3·3–5·0 mm. "Black carpet beetle"................................
..........................(*A. megatoma* F.) **Attagenus piceus** Olivier
10. Species 1·5–3·0 mm. Each eye evenly rounded. Elytra unicolorous or
nearly so. "Khapra beetle".......................................
.....................(*T. khapra* =) **Trogoderma granarium** Everts
Species 2·5–5·0 mm. Each eye (fig. 36) with inner margin distinctly emarginate. Elytra black or dark brown with irregular pale brown markings which are clothed with nearly white hairs. "Larger cabinet beetle"
..................................**Trogoderma inclusum** Le Conte

CLERIDAE

The Cleridae or "chequered beetles" comprise a rather large
family of more than 2,000 species, most of which are tropical. They
are brightly coloured and pubescent insects of moderate size. The
antennae are usually 11-segmented and the apical segments are
enlarged or form a distinct club. The elytra always completely cover
the abdomen in those species dealt with here, and there are five or
six ventral abdominal segments. The tarsi are all 5-segmented, but
the first and fourth segments are often very small. Probably nearly

all the species are predacious, but a few, e.g. *Necrobia rufipes*, also feed on cured meats, especially ham, bacon, and smoked pork and old cheeses, as well as on oil seeds. Most of the ten or so species that have been found associated with stored food products are predacious and in that sense beneficial. *Thaneroclerus buqueti*, for example, has been recorded as a predator of *Lasioderma serricorne*.

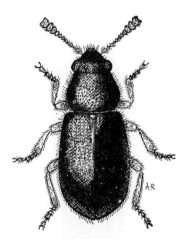

FIG. 47.—*Necrobia rufipes* Degeer. ×7

1. Whole of dorsal and ventral surface as well as legs dark brown. (Prothorax with a short and narrow but very distinct basal neck.) 5–6·5 mm. . . . . . .
. . . .**Thanoclerus buqueti** Lefevre
Elytra entirely or partly blue or blue-green; sometimes with a transverse yellow or ivory-white band just behind middle .2
2. Elytra with a transverse yellow or ivory-white band just behind middle (fig. 48). The head and pronotum are red. The basal sides as well as the apical third of the elytra are sometimes reddish instead of blue. Hind tarsi with fourth segment minute and scarcely visible. 5–7 mm.
. . . .**Paratillus carus** Newman*
Elytra without a yellow or ivory-white transverse band. 3
3. Prothorax and basal fourth of elytra reddish brown. 4–6 mm. . . . .
. . . .**Necrobia ruficollis** Fabricius
Dorsal surface entirely blue or blue-green 4
4. Antennae and legs everywhere black or bluish. 4–4·5 mm. . . . .
. . . .**Necrobia violacea** Linnaeus
Basal segments of antennae and all of legs yellowish or red 5

---

* *Tarsostenus univittatus* Rossi resembles *P. carus* in colour but the pronotum is usually bluish and the head is always dark brown, black, or bluish.

5. Eyes separated dorsally by much more than the width of an eye (fig. 47)r
  Antennal club dark brown or black; apical segment of antenna not longe.
  than broad. Legs red. Abdomen beneath everywhere dark blue. 4–5 mm.
  "Copra beetle" or "red-legged ham beetle" ....
  ....**Necrobia rufipes** Degeer
  Eyes separated dorsally by not more than the width of one eye. Antennal
  club yellowish brown; apical segment of antenna three times as long as
  broad. Abdomen beneath paler reddish or yellowish near apex. 4–5 mm.
  ....**Exkorynetes analis** Klug

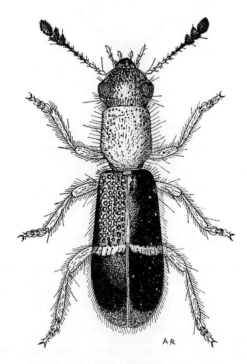

Fig. 48.—*Paratillus carus* Newman.   ×12

ANOBIIDAE

The Anobiidae, sometimes known as "furniture beetles," include
more than 1,000 species of which the majority are confined to the
tropics. They are small, subcylindrical, oval, or nearly globular
beetles with the prothorax more or less covering the deflexed head.
In the species dealt with here the antennae are 11-segmented with a
loose 3-segmented club or else with the last eight segments enlarged.

The elytra completely cover the abdomen, and there are five visible ventral segments. All tarsi are 5-segmented, segments 1–4 decreasing in length. The larvae usually live in dry wood, but a number of species occur in dry animal matter, stored food products, drugs, and tobacco. About 15 species have been recorded in stored food, warehouses, etc., in various parts of the world. Some of these, e.g. *Anobium punctatum*, occur in warehouses and granaries only because they happen to be boring in the woodwork.

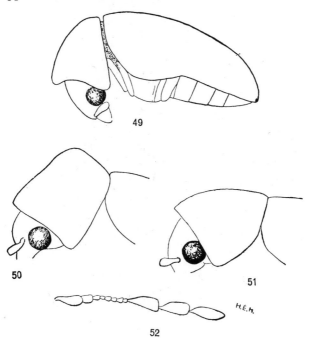

FIGS. 49–52.—(49) *Lasioderma serricorne* Fabricius. (50) *Anobium punctatum* Degeer. (51) *Stegobium paniceum* Linnaeus. (52) Antenna of *Anobium punctatum* Degeer

1. Antennae with segments 4–10 serrate. Elytra not striate (fig. 49). 2–2·5 mm. Cigarette beetle" ....**Lasioderma serricorne** Fabricius
   Antennae (fig. 52) with a large and loose 3-segmented club. Elytra distinctly striate 2
2. Prothorax with basal middle part, when seen from side, very strongly humped (fig. 50). 3–5 mm. "Common furniture beetle"...............
   ....(*A. domesticum* = *A. striatum* =) **Anobium punctatum** Degeer (fig. 53)
   Prothorax with basal middle part not humped (fig. 51). 2–3 mm. "Drug store beetle".......(*Sitodrepa panicea* =) **Stegobium paniceum** Linnaeus

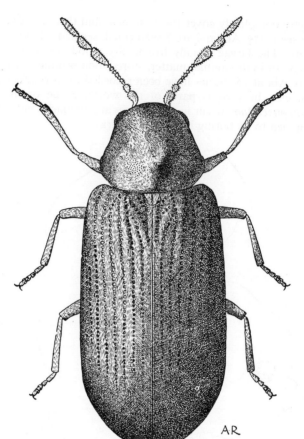

Fig. 53.—*Anobium punctatum* Degeer.   ×22

PTINIDAE*

The Ptinidae include about 500 species of small beetles closely related to the Anobiidae. Because of their long legs and antennae, stout bodies, and hairy surface they resemble small spiders and are often known as "spider beetles". The antennae are placed on the front of the head between the eyes and are generally rather close together. They are 11-segmented and are never thickened apically.

---

* The Ptinidae of economic importance are dealt with in more detail by Hinton, H. E., 1941, *Bull. Ent. Res.*, **31**, 331–381, 59 figs.

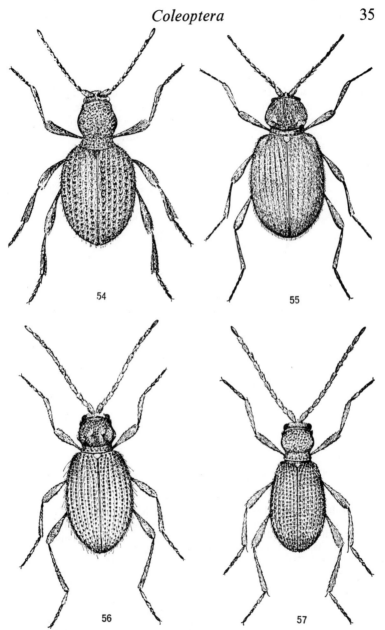

FIGS. 54–57.—(54) *Pseudeurostus hilleri* Reitter. ×16. (55) *Ptinus tectus* Boieldieu ×12. (56) *Ptinus clavipes* Panzer. ×13. (57) *Ptinus pusillus* Sturm. ×15. (After Hinton, 1941)

The base of the prothorax has a short and more or less narrow constriction or neck. The elytra completely cover the abdomen, and there are four or five visible ventral abdominal segments. All tarsi are 5-segmented, segments 1–4 decreasing in length. About 24 species have been found associated with stored food products in various parts of the world. Of these, eight species are frequently met with in granaries and warehouses in this country.

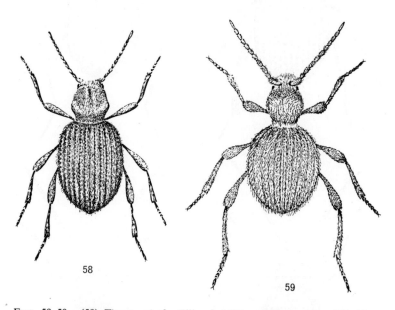

58

59

Figs. 58–59.—(58) *Tipnus unicolor* Piller & Mitterpacher. ×15. (59) *Niptus hololeucus* Faldermann. ×9. (After Hinton, 1941)

1. Breadth of elevated part of head between bases of antennae equal to a fourth or less of length of first antennal segment (figs. 54–57)..........2
   Breadth of elevated part of head between bases of antennae equal to more than half of length of first antennal segment (fig. 59) 6
2. Scutellum small, indistinct, and almost vertical (fig. 54). 1·9–2·8 mm.
   ....**Pseudeurostus hilleri** Reitter
   Scutellum large, very distinct, and on same plane as adjacent parts of elytra 3
3. Elytra so densely clothed with brown or golden-brown hairs that strial punctures and intervals are not distinct unless specimen is rubbed (fig. 55). 2·5–4·0 mm. "Australian spider beetle".......**Ptinus tectus** Boieldieu
   Elytra much more sparsely hairy so that strial punctures and intervals are always distinctly visible 4

4. Prothorax with a longitudinal, feebly oblique, dense cushion of paler hairs on each side of middle near base. (Elytra with white scales. Second ventral abdominal segment with punctures three times as long as broad.) 2·0–4·3 mm. "White-marked spider beetle" . . . . **Ptinus fur** Linnaeus
Prothorax with hairs more or less evenly distributed, not forming dense cushions 5
5. Elytra without white hairs or scales. Middle of second abdominal sternite with punctures elongate, about three times as long as broad. Male with apical tibial spurs short and straight (fig. 56). 2·3–3·2 m . "Brown spider beetle" . . . . (*P. hirtellus* Sturm. =) **Ptinus clavipes** Panzer
Elytra with at least a few white scales or hairs. Middle of second ventral segment of abdomen with punctures round or broadly oval. Male with apical tibial spurs, particularly of middle and hind legs, very long and strongly curved (fig. 57). 1·8–3·0 mm. . . . . **Ptinus pusillus** Sturm
6. Elytra moderately densely hairy, the striae and strial punctures being deep, coarse, and very distinct (fig. 58). 1·8–3·0 mm. . . . .
. . . . **Tipnus unicolor** Piller & Mitterpacher
Elytra very densely hairy, without striae, and with punctures completely concealed by hairs 7
7. Elytra greyish or yellow-brown with patches of darker, often nearly black, hairs. Prothorax with a broad, nearly complete, median longitudinal depression. 2·0–4·0 mm. . . . . **Trigonogenius globulus** Solier
Elytra and prothorax uniformly clothed with golden-yellow hairs. Prothorax (fig. 59) without a longitudinal depression. 3·0–4·5 mm. "Golden spider beetle" . . . . **Niptus hololeucus** Faldermann

TENEBRIONIDAE

This is one of the largest and most important families of beetles. They are small to moderately large insects nearly always uniformly black or dark brown in colour. The 11-segmented (rarely 10-segmented) antennae are inserted under the sides of the head or under a frontal ridge and are thickened or even clubbed near their apices. The elytra completely cover the abdomen, and there are five visible ventral abdominal segments. The front and middle tarsi are 5-segmented and the hind tarsi 4-segmented. The tarsal segmentation alone will serve to distinguish the members of this family from nearly all others found on stored food products. The majority feed on decaying vegetable matter, a number feed on various parts of living plants, and a few are predacious. More than 100 species have been found in various parts of the world associated with stored food products, and of these about 14 commonly occur in Britain.

1. Species about one inch long. Black. Side margin of head not produced backwards and not dividing the very narrow eyes. Antenna with third segment considerably more than twice as long as fourth. Elytra not striate and apices strongly and narrowly produced behind. 20–24 mm. "Churchyard beetle" . . . . **Blaps mucronata** Latreille

Species much less than one inch, rarely as much as $\frac{1}{2}$ inch long. Brown
or reddish brown, rarely black. Side margins of head dividing eyes
except in *Palorus*. Antenna with third segment usually only slightly
longer than fourth, rarely (*Tenebrio obscurus*) nearly twice as long as
fourth. Elytra striate and apices never narrowly produced 2
2. Elytra reddish brown with base, a broad median band, and a narrower
subapical band black. 2·2–2·5 mm. "Two-banded fungus beetle"......
......................................**Alphitophagus bifasciatus** Say
Elytra unicolorous 3

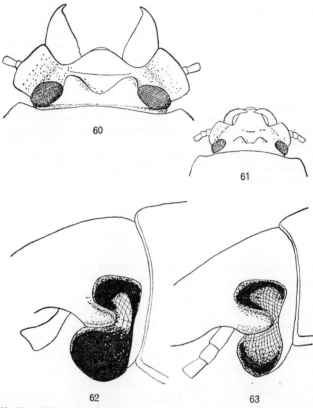

FIGS. 60–63.—(60) Male of *Gnathocerus cornutus* Fabricius.   (61) Same of *G.
maxillosus* Fabricius.   (62) Eye of *Alphitobius diaperinus* Panzer.   (63) Same
of *A. laevigatus* Fabricius.

3. Species about $\frac{1}{2}$ inch (14–18 mm.) long.............................4
Species $\frac{1}{4}$ inch long or less (7 mm. maximum).......................5
4. Antenna with apical segment as long as broad and third segment only
slightly (12 : 10) longer than fourth. Dorsal surface feebly shining.
15 mm. "Yellow mealworm" ....**Tenebrio molitor** Linnaeus

Antenna with apical segment broader than long and third segment nearly twice as long as fourth. Dorsal surface not shining. 14–18 mm. "Dark mealworm"..............................**Tenebrio obscurus** Fabricius

5. Species 4·5–7 mm. long, rather broad (relatively much broader than the species of *Tribolium*, fig. 64), and usually black or dark brown........6
   Species usually less than 4·5 mm. long (except *Tribolium destructor* which is 5–6 mm.); body narrow, subcylindrical, and *Tribolium*-like (fig. 64) in appearance; colour reddish brown, rarely (*Tribolium destructor*) black..7

6. Eyes completely or nearly completely divided (fig. 63) by backwardly produced side margin of head, the narrowest point being equal to the breadth of a single facet. Antenna with fifth segment subparallel, inner apex not produced. Anterior tibia with apex only feebly broadened. 4·5–6 mm. "Black fungus beetle"....................................
   ....(*A. piceus* Olivier =) **Alphitobius laevigatus** Fabricius

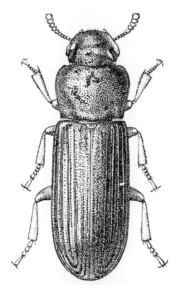

Fig. 64.—*Tribolium confusum* Jacquelin du Val. ×15

Eyes only partly divided (fig. 62), the narrowest point being equal to the combined breath of three or four facets. Antenna with inner apex of fifth segment feebly produced. Anterior tibia with apex strongly broadened. 5·5–7 mm. ....
......(*A. piceus* & *A. ovatus* of authors=) **Alphitobius diaperinus** Panzer

7. Eyes not divided by side margin of head and more or less round........8
   Eyes always partly divided by backwardly produced side margin of head and with vertical diameter always much greater than horizontal 9

8. Head with anterior sides not strongly explanate or flexed upwards; ridge above eyes feeble and indistinct. Eyes small and round. 2·5–3 mm. "Small-eyed flour beetle" ....
......................**Palorus** (=*Caenocorse*) **ratzeburgii** Wissmann

Head with anterior sides strongly explanate and flexed upwards; ridge above eyes distinct and covering anterior part of eyes. Eyes large and vertical diameter slightly but distinctly larger than horizontal. 2·5 mm. "Depressed flour beetle" ....
.....................**Palorus** (=*Caenocorse*) **subdepressus** Wollaston

9. Antenna shorter than head and with a very distinct, compact, 5-segmented club (fig. 65). Side margin of head not extending more than a fourth of the distance across the eyes. Hind tarsi with basal segment not as long as the combined length of the two following. 2·5–3 mm. "Long-headed flour beetle" ....**Latheticus oryzae** Waterhouse

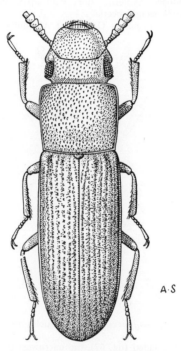

A·S

FIG. 65.—*Latheticus oryzae* Waterhouse. ×32

Antenna distinctly longer than head and with a compact 3-segmented club, or a loose 4-segmented club, or gradually broadened from base to apex and without a club. Backwardly produced side margin of head extending half or more than half of distance across eyes. Hind tarsi with basal segment as long as combined length of two following 10

10. Elytra with at least lateral intervals finely but distinctly keeled (fig. 64). Males without distinct tubercles on head and without large, upwardly curved teeth on mandibles 11

Elytra with all intervals quite flat. Male with two prominent tubercles on middle of head and each mandible with a large, conspicuous curved tooth directed upwards 13

11. Antennae with a distinct, moderately compact, 3-segmented club. 3–4 mm. (Head without a ridge above eyes; eyes separated ventrally by much less than two diameters of an eye.) "Rust-red flour beetle" (*T. ferrugineum* & *T. navale* Auctt. =) **Tribolium castaneum** Herbst
    Antennae with loose, indistinct, 5- or 6-segmented club or without a club and only gradually thickened towards apex 12

12. Species 4–4·5 mm. Reddish brown. (Head with a ridge above eyes; eyes separated ventrally by a space equal to three times diameter of an eye.) "Confused flour beetle".... **Tribolium confusum** Jacquelin du Val (fig. 64)
    Species 5–6 mm. Black or very dark brown ....
    .... **Tribolium destructor** Uyttenboogaart

13. Male with dorsal tooth of mandible much broader at base than near apex, these teeth being about as broad as the distance between them (fig. 60); clypeus with anterior margin strongly rounded; sides of head everywhere very broadly explanate and strongly flexed upwards. Female with broadest point of head before eyes. 3·5–4·5 mm. "Broad-horned flour beetle" .... **Gnathocerus cornutus** Fabricius
    Male with dorsal tooth of mandible nearly round in cross-section and only slightly narrowed to apex, these teeth being less than half as broad as distance between them (fig. 61); clypeus with anterior margin truncate; sides of head much less strongly explanate and then only anterior to instead of also opposite eye. Female with broadest point of head across posterior parts of eyes. 3–4 mm. "Slender-horned flour beetle" .... **Gnathocerus maxillosus** Fabricius

LEPIDOPTERA

The Lepidoptera (butterflies and moths) are one of the best known and most easily recognised Orders of insects. About 150,000 species have been described. They have two pairs of membranous wings, and these as well as the body and legs nearly always are densely clothed with broad scales, which are coloured and often form definite patterns. The mandibles are reduced to non-functional lobes or are absent, and the maxillae are nearly always modified to form a long sucking tube or *proboscis*, which lies coiled beneath the head when not in use. By means of this proboscis they are able to suck up fluids. Metamorphosis is complete. The caterpillars have a well-developed head, three thoracic and ten distinct abdominal segments. Their mouth-parts are adapted for biting, and feeding is almost entirely confined to this stage. There are nearly always three pairs of

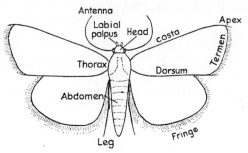

Fig. 66.—Diagram showing parts of a moth

5-segmented thoracic legs. Those found in stored foods may be immediately distinguished from the larvae of all other insects occurring in similar situations by having paired pseudopods or prolegs on abdominal segments 3–6 and 10. Each of these prolegs is armed with fine, curved, apical "teeth," called crochets, which are usually arranged in the form of a circle.

The moths, the larvae of which infest stored products, are rather small and thus not easily identified. In general, moths can be identified by means of the pattern on the wings, and to do this it is necessary to know the names of the more important parts of the wings. The margin of the wing nearest the head is the *costa*, that nearest the body is the *dorsum* and that farthest from the body is the *termen*: the costa and the termen meet at the *apex* (fig. 66). With the exception of *Paralipsa gularis*, both sexes of all the moths listed in the key have similar wing patterns.

Two structural characters which are employed in the key are the form of the labial palpi and the position of vein 8 on the hindwing.

The *labial palpi* (figs. 67–69) are paired, 3-segmented appendages visible in front of the head and arising between the eyes beneath the head. These organs are not to be confused with the much longer thread-like antennae situated above the eyes or with the legs attached to the underside of the thorax. In some species, paired segmented maxillary palpi are present, situated one on each side of the base of the proboscis, but these structures are not as long or as robust as the labial palpi.

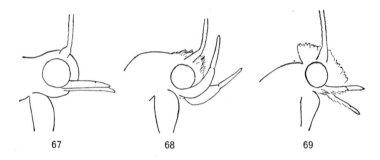

67   68   69

FIGS. 67–69.—(67) Head and labial palpi of female of *Corcyra cephalonica* Stainton. (68) Same of *Endrosis sarcitrella* Linnaeus. (69) Same of *Tinea pallescentella* Stainton

It is not always easy to examine the veins of a small moth, although the venation of larger moths can usually be seen without difficulty after the application of toluene, xylene or alcohol to the wing surface. The venation of the hind wing can be studied conveniently by detaching a wing and placing it on a glass slide beneath a cover-slip and allowing a drop of xylene, etc. to flow under the cover-slip. The venation can then be seen with a ×15 hand-lens. Usually the costal area of the hindwing is more densely scaled in the Pyralidae than it is in the other families considered here (Tineidae, Tortricidae, Oeco-phoridae, Gelechiidae), and if vein 8 does not stand out clearly after the treatment described above, the probability is that the moth belongs to the Pyralidae and not to the Tineidae etc.

As far as they are represented by these economic species, vein 8 on the hindwing arises at the base of the wing above the cell and runs more or less parallel with the costa as far as the apex. In the Tineidae etc., vein 8 is free throughout its length, and is situated nearer the

44   Common Insect Pests of Stored Food Products

costal margin than the upper edge of the cell (fig. 70). In the Pyralidae, vein 8 is very near the upper border of the cell, and, in all the species dealt with here except *Pyralis farinalis* and *Hypsopygia costalis*, it is united with vein 7 beyond the cell, but separates from it again before reaching the costa (figs. 71–72).

The eggs are deposited by the female moth on or in the food material and the larvae usually remain in the same spot until fully

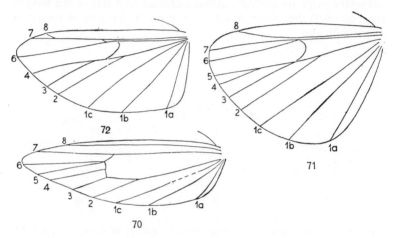

Figs. 70–72.—(70) Venation of hindwing of *Tinea pellionella* Linnaeus.   (71) Same of *Pyralis farinalis* Linnaeus.   (72) Same of *Ephestia elutella* Hübner

fed when, in the case of many species, they wander off to seek a crevice in which to pupate. It is usually at such times that the larvae come under observation. In some species, such as *Tinea pellionella*, the larva lives in a portable case made of silk. In all the species dealt with here, the pupa is enclosed within a silken cocoon constructed by the larva before pupation.

In a warm warehouse one generation of moths may succeed another without much regard to season, but in the open in this country a moth is usually only single- or double-brooded, one generation spending the winter as quiescent larvae or pupae and the following brood undergoing its transformations rapidly to produce moths in the autumn.

Moth pests of stored products are comparatively small insects and the families to which they belong are cosmopolitan. Their larvae have diverse habits, frequently living concealed. A large number of species in these families are of considerable economic importance.

Key to Moths*

1. Hindwing with the fringe short, the hairs less than half as long as the breadth of the wing.† Hindwing with vein 8 very near to the upper margin of the cell and approaching or uniting with vein 7 beyond the cell-end (figs. 71 and 72) . . . . **Pyralidae** 2
   Hindwing with the fringe long, the hairs at least as long as half the breadth of the wing. Hindwing with vein 8 quite separate from vein 7 and nearer to the costa than to the upper margin of the cell (fig. 70) (in *Sitotroga cerealella* vein 8 touches the upper margin of the cell beyond the middle) . . . . **Tineidae** 9

2. Labial palpi prominent and curved upwards 3
   Labial palpi inconspicuous in males of *Corcyra cephalonica* and *Paralipsa gularis*, but conspicuous in the remainder, where they are more or less straight in front of the head or slightly curved downwards (fig. 67) 7

3. Upper side of hindwing coloured (either smoky black or pale crimson purple) and crossed by two narrow irregular pale lines. Upper side of forewing with a coloured pattern. Male without a costal fold on the underside of the forewing 4
   Upper side of hindwing greyish white or greyish buff and unmarked. Upper side of forewing dull greyish brown with markings obscure but, usually, an inner dark line or band (with the inner edge pale in some species), and an outer pale or dark band across the wing can be distinguished. Male with a costal fold in the basal third of the underside of the forewing, this fold covering a brush-like tuft which can be expanded (this costal fold absent in *Ephestia*‡ *kuehniella*)§ 5,

4. Upper side of both wings with yellow fringes. Upper side pale crimson-purple, the forewing with two yellow spots on the costal margin, and the hindwing crossed by two narrow yellow lines. "The gold fringe" . . . . **Hypsopygia costalis** Fabricius (fig. 81)

---

* For an account of all the species infesting stored food products, see Corbet, A. S., and Tams, W. H. T., 1943, "Keys for the Identification of the Lepidoptera infesting Stored Food Products," *Proc. zool. Soc. Lond.*, **(B) 113**, 55–148, 287 figs.

‡ *Anagasta* and *Cadra* are now considered to be subgenera of *Ephestia* and the names are not used in the present issue.

† In the male of *Corcyra cephalonica* the hindwing fringe is rather long towards the abdomen, but it is never as long as half the breadth of the wing.

§ The three species considered here have the wing pattern so similar that identification of rubbed specimens may be difficult or impossible by reference to the pattern. In these species, the male and female genital organs differ distinctly from one species to another, and if the genitalia are extruded by gentle pressure on the abdomen (from the middle outwards) in a recently captured or relaxed specimen, it is not difficult to see the salient characters by means of a hand-lens.

In the male, the important characters are the shape of the valves (figs. 94–97) and the ventral view of the uncus (figs. 98–101). In the female, a glance at the ovipositor (figs. 102–105), which is often found extruded in dead specimens, may be sufficient to differentiate between the three species. The genitalia of *Plodia interpunctella* are figured for comparison.

These characters may also be studied by warming the entire abdomen, after removal from the specimen, in a 10% caustic potash solution. The cleared abdomen may then be examined in water or alcohol.

Upper side fringes not yellow. Upper side of forewing pale ochreous buff, with basal and apical areas purple-brown, the pale central area divided from the darker areas by narrow white lines: upper side of hindwing smoky black, crossed by two narrow whitish lines. "The meal moth" ....**Pyralis farinalis** Linnaeus (fig. 82)

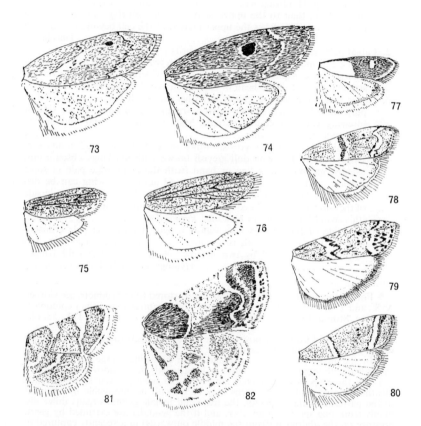

Figs. 73–82.—Wing patterns in the Pyralidae. (73) Male of *Paralipsa gularis* Zeller. (74) Female of *Paralipsa gularis* Zeller. (75) Male of *Corcyra cephalonica* Stainton. (76) Female of *Corcyra cephalonica* Stainton. (77) *Plodia interpunctella* Hübner. (78) *Ephestia cautella* Walker. (79) *Ephestia kuehniella* Zeller. (80) *Ephestia elutella* Hübner. (81) *Hypsopygia costalis* Fabricius. (82) *Pyralis farinalis* Linnaeus. (All ×3 approximately.)

5. Upper side of forewing with the outer band well defined, rather sinuate pale and bordered on each side by a narrow dark line, the dark bordering

more intense near the costa. "The cacao moth" . . . .
. . . .**Ephestia elutella** Hübner (fig. 80)*
Upper side of forewing with the outer band very obscure and not well
defined 6

6. Upper side of forewing with the inner band dark and straight (at right-
angles to the dorsum), rather broad and continuous, and with a broad
pale band along its inner edge. Male with a costal fold on underside
of forewing. "The dried currant moth" . . . .
. . . .**Ephestia cautella** Walker (fig. 78)
Upper side of forewing with the inner band oblique, rather irregular and
consisting of dark streaks or spots, and without a pale band along its
inner edge. Male without a costal fold on underside of forewing. "The
Mediterranean flour moth" . . . .
. . . .**Ephestia kuehniella** Zeller (fig. 79)†

7. Upper side of forewing with the basal third pale yellowish buff, this pale
area separated from the outer reddish brown area by a dark brown
line. Head without a projecting tuft of scales. Labial palpi not remark-
ably long. "The Indian meal moth" . . . .
. . . .**Plodia interpunctella** Hübner (fig. 77)
Upper side of forewing uniformly coloured pale buff brown. Head with a
projecting tuft of scales. Labial palpi very short and inconspicuous in
the male, long and prominent in the female (fig. 67) . . . . : 8

8. Upper side of forewing without spots, but with the veins slightly darkened.
Upper side of hindwing darker in the male than in the female . . . .
. . . .**Corcyra cephalonica** Stainton (figs. 75 and 76)
Upper side of forewing with a black spot at or beyond the centre of the
wing. The male has a reddish yellow streak in the centre of the fore-
wing which is absent in the female . . . .
. . . .**Paralipsa gularis** Zeller (figs. 73 and 74)

9. Labial palpi long, sickle-shaped, sharply pointed, and pointing upwards
(fig. 68). Head smooth 10
Labial palpi shorter, rather blunt, straight, or nearly straight, projecting
in front of the head, and either horizontal or sloping downwards (fig. 69).
Head rough haired 12

10. Hindwing apex very elongate, sharply pointed and needle-like. Upper side
of forewing pale ochreous brown, and usually a black dot can be seen
beyond the centre of the wing; upper side of hindwing with a whitish stripe
running from the wing base to beyond the centre for about two-thirds the
length of the wing. "The Angoumois grain moth" . . . .
. . . .**Sitotroga cerealella** Olivier (figs. 84 and 85)
Hindwing apex may be pointed but is not needle-like. Upper side of hind-
wing without a whitish central stripe 11

---

* The hair-scales in the costal fold are blackish in *E. elutella* and yellowish
in *E. cautella*; in *E. elutella* the inner band on the forewing is oblique, as in
E. kuehniella.
† In recent years *Ephestia calidella* Guenée has frequently been imported in
stored products from Mediterranean countries. It traces to couplet 6 of the
key. It is like *Ephestia kuehniella* Zeller in that the inner band of the upper
side of the forewing is not straight, but the male has a costal fold on the underside of the forewing. The genitalia of both sexes are shown in figs. 110–111.

48 Common Insect Pests of Stored Food Products

11. Head and at least the front of the thorax conspicuously white; labial palpi mostly white, with tips blackened. Upper side of forewing shining buff, speckled with dark brown, and usually with two or three blackish spots. "The white-shouldered house moth" ....
............................**Endrosis sarcitrella** Linnaeus (fig. 86)
Head, thorax and labial palpi brown. Upper side of forewing buff-brown to dark buff-brown, with three more or less distinct dark brown spots,

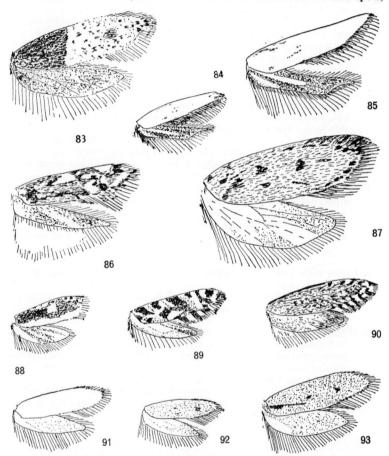

FIGS. 83–93.—Wing patterns. (83) *Trichophaga tapetzella* Linnaeus. (84) Male of *Sitotroga cerealella* Olivier. (85) Female of *Sitotroga cerealella* Olivier. (86) *Endrosis sarcitrella* Linnaeus. (87) *Hofmannophila pseudospretella* Stainton. (88) *Monopis crocicapitella* Clemens. (89) *Nemapogon granella* Linnaeus. (90) *Haplotinea ditella* Pierce & Metcalfe. (91) *Tineola bisselliella* Hummel. (92) *Tinea pellionella* Linnaeus. (93) *Tinea pallescentella* Stainton. (All ×3 approximately.)

one just beyond the centre of the wing and two (one above the other) between the central spot and the base of the wing. "The brown house moth"............**Hofmannophila pseudospretella** Stainton (fig. 87)
12. Upper side of forewing with the basal third deep chocolate-brown contrasting sharply with the whitish outer two-thirds, and with the wing apex slightly darkened. "The white-tip clothes moth" ....
.........................**Trichophaga tapetzella** Linnaeus (fig. 83)

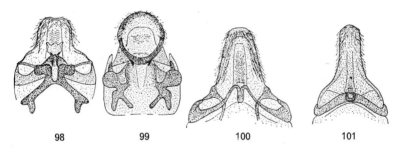

FIGS. 94–101. Male genitalia—(94) Valve of *Ephestia elutella* Hübner. (95) Same of *Ephestia cautella* Walker. (96) Same of *Ephestia kuehniella* Zeller. (97) Same of *Plodia interpunctella* Hübner. (98) Ventral view of uncus of *Ephestia elutella* Hübner. (99) Same of *Ephestia cautella* Walker. (100) Same of *Ephestia kuehniella* Zeller. (101) Same of *Plodia interpunctella* Hübner

Upper side of forewing more or less uniformly coloured and not sharply divided into two strongly contrasted zones.......................13
13. Upper side of forewing dark brown, with a slightly mottled appearance and a clearly defined cream-coloured central spot 14
Upper side of forewing not dark brown and without a clearly defined cream-coloured central spot 15
14. Upper side of forewing with a yellowish white stripe along the dorsum....
............................**Monopis crocicapitella** Clemens (fig. 88)

50   Common Insect Pests of Stored Food Products

Upper side of forewing without a pale stripe along the dorsum ....
....**Monopis rusticella** Clerck
15. Upper side of forewing pale ochreous buff, entirely unmarked and without
   dark dusting. "The common clothes moth" ....
   ....**Tineola bisselliella** Hummel (fig. 91)
   Upper side of forewing with dark markings and some dark dusting......16
16. Upperside of forewing with about six dark reddish-brown or chocolate-
   brown costal spots; ground colour buff with dark dusting and irregular
   brown markings (fig. 89) ....**Nemapogon granella** Linnaeus*
   Upper side of forewing without a prominent central chain of dark spots. .17

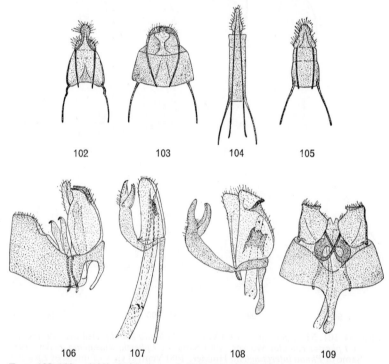

102   103   104   105

106   107   108   109

Figs. 102–109.—(102) Ovipositor of *Ephestia elutella* Hübner. (103) Same of
Ephestia cautella Walker. (104) Same of *Ephestia kuehniella* Zeller.
(105) Same of *Plodia interpunctella* Hübner. (106) Male genitalia of
Nemapogon granella Linnaeus (lateral view). (107) Same of *Tinea pellionella*
Linnaeus (lateral view). (108) Same of *Niditinea fuscipunctella* Haworth
(lateral view). (109) Same of *Haplotinea ditella* Pierce & Metcalfe (central
view)

---

   * *Nemapogon granella* typifies a small group of moths (of which several
are British) which are similar in appearance and often difficult or impossible
to separate without examination of the genitalia. All are liable to occur in
stored products.

17. Upper side of forewing pale shining buff, sparsely dusted with dark dots, and the costa not chequered near the apex: usually three small but distinct dark spots are present and these comprise a central spot about one-third of the wing length from the termen, and two spots (or a spot and a streak), one above the other, between the central spot and the base of the wing 18
Upper side of forewing heavily dusted with dark dots, and the costal margin faintly chequered near the apex 19
18. Upper side of forewing with the lower inner spot prolonged to a prominent dark narrow streak, and the sparse dark dusting irregularly distributed Length of forewing 7–10 mm. "The large pale clothes moth" ....
.............................**Tinea pallescentella** Stainton (fig. 93)

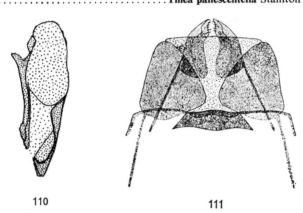

110   111

FIGS. 110–111.—(110) Valve of *Ephestia calidella* Guenée. (111) Ovipositor of same. (Fig. 111 after Richards and Thompson, 1932)

Upper side of forewing with the lower inner spot not prolonged to a dark streak, and the dark dusting uniformly distributed. Length of forewing less than 6 mm. "The case-bearing clothes moth" ....
.............................**Tinea pellionella** Linnaeus (fig. 92)*
19. Upper side of forewing with the usual three dark spots found in *T. pellionella*, and the lower inner spot prolonged to a dark streak; ground colour buff, dusted with dark brown dots, but with the markings clearly visible. Upper side of hindwing shining yellowish white. "The brown-dotted clothes moth" ....**Niditinea fuscipunctella** Haworth
Upper side of forewing without the three dark spots found in *T. pellionella*: ground colour dark brownish buff, heavily dark dusted, and the markings not clearly defined. Upper side of hindwing with a purple sheen ....
.....................**Haplotinea ditella** Pierce & Metcalfe (fig. 90)†

---

* The *Tinea pellionella* group is represented by three British species which are difficult to identify without examination of the genitalia. All may occur in stored products.
† *Haplotinea ditella* can only be satisfactorily separated from the similar *H. insectella* Fabricius, which may also occur in stored products, by examination of the genitalia.

Key to Larvae*

1. Abdominal prolegs short, narrow, and often very indistinct; each with not more than two crochets. Always inside the grain kernels except in the first instar . . . .**Sitotroga cerealella** Olivier
   Abdominal prolegs well developed and each with many crochets 2
2. Two setae in front of prothoracic spiracle (fig. 112) 3
   Three setae in front of prothoracic spiracle (fig. 113) 10

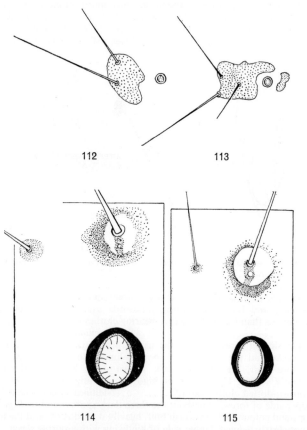

112   113

114   115

Figs. 112–115. Larval segments—(112) Prothoracic spiracle of *Ephestia elutella* Hübner. (113) Same of *Tinea pellionella* Linnaeus. (114) Eighth abdominal spiracle and setae of *Paralipsa gularis* Zeller. (115) Eighth abdominal spiracle and setae of *Corcyra cephalonica* Stainton

* For keys dealing with a much larger number of species, including some not yet found in Britain, see Hinton, H. E., 1943, "The larvae of the Lepidoptera associated with stored products," *Bull. ent. Res.*, **34**, 163–212, 128 figs.

3. First abdominal segment (as shown for eighth segment, fig. 114) with a
   sclerotised or pigmented ring enclosing a membranous area around the
   base of the seta immediately above the spiracle (Gallerinae)............4
   First abdominal segment without a pigmented ring enclosing a membranous
   area around the base of the seta immediately above the spiracle 5
4. Abdominal spiracles (fig. 114) with opposite sides of rim (peritreme) more or
   less equally thickened. Cuticle of abdomen usually creamy yellow or
   yellowish grey.............................**Paralipsa gularis** Zeller

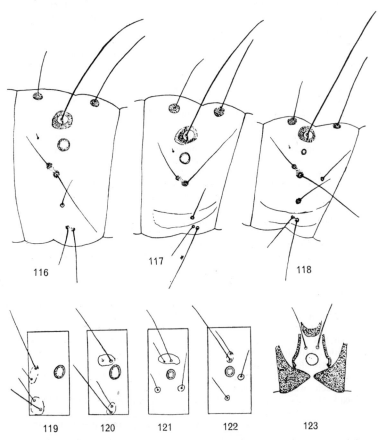

FIGS. 116–123. Larval segments—(116) Eighth abdominal segment of *Ephestia
kuehniella* Zeller. (117) Same of *Ephestia cautella* Walker. (118) Same of
Ephestia elutella Hübner. (119) Spiracle and associated setae of eighth
abdominal segment of *Laspeyresia pomonella* Linnaeus. (120) Same of
Hofmannophila pseudospretella Stainton. (121) Same of *Tinea pellionella*
Linnaeus. (122) Spiracle and associated setae of seventh abdominal segment
of *Monopis rusticella* Clerck. (123) Ventral view of labium of *Endrosis
sarcitrella* Linnaeus

Abdominal spiracles (fig. 115) with posterior part of rim distinctly thicker
than anterior part. Cuticle of abdomen usually white . . . .
. . . . **Corcyra cephalonica** Stainton
5. Mesothorax with a sclerotised or pigmented ring enclosing a membranous
   area around the base of the fourth seta from the mid-dorsal line. Head
   with six ocelli on each side and abdomen never olive-brown mottled with
   darker patches (Phycitinae). 6
   Mesothorax without sclerotised or pigmented rings around the bases of
   any of the setae. Head with four ocelli (*Pyralis*), or, if with six (*Hypsopygia*), the abdomen is olive-brown mottled with darker patches
   (Pyralinae) 9
6. Setae of first seven abdominal segments not arising from pigmented areas of
   the cuticle . . . . **Plodia interpunctella** Hübner
   Setae of first seven abdominal segments arising from round or oval pig-
   mented areas of the cuticle 7
7. Eighth abdominal segment (fig. 117) with the minute seta in front of the
   spiracle separated from the spiracle by a distance equal to distinctly
   less, or very slightly more, than the diameter of the spiracle*. . . . .
   . . . . **Ephestia cautella** Walker
   Eighth abdominal segment (figs. 116, 118) with the minute seta in front
   of the spiracle separated from the spiracle by a distance equal to nearly
   two or even three times the diameter of the spiracle 8
8. Eighth abdominal segment with spiracle (fig. 116) as broad as or broader
   than the membranous area enclosed by the pigmented ring around the
   base of the seta immediately above the spiracle . . . .
   . . . . **Ephestia kuehniella** Zeller†
   Eighth abdominal segment with spiracle (fig. 118) not more than two-
   thirds as broad as the membranous area enclosed by the pigmented ring
   around the base of the seta immediately above the spiracle . . . .
   . . . . **Ephestia elutella** Hübner
9. Head with four ocelli on each side. Mandible without a ventral subapical
   tooth. Cuticle of abdomen whitish or greyish with second to seventh
   abdominal segments usually distinctly paler than others . . . .
   . . . . **Pyralis farinalis** Linnaeus
   Head with six ocelli on each side. Mandible with a large, ventral, sub-
   apical tooth. Cuticle of abdomen olive-brown mottled with darker
   patches . . . . **Hypsopygia costalis** Fabricius
10. Eighth abdominal segment (fig. 120) with the first two setae below the
    spiracle close together 11
    Eighth abdominal segment (fig. 121) with the first two setae below the
    spiracle widely separated 13
11. Head with six ocelli on each side. Eighth abdominal segment (fig. 119)
    with a long seta immediately in front of the spiracle . . . .
    . . . . (*Cydia pomonella* =) **Laspeyresia pomonella** Linnaeus

---

* The larva of *Ephestia calidella* Guenée traces in this key to *Ephestia cautella*
Walker, but most specimens may be distinguished from the latter species by
having the seventh abdominal spiracle intermediate in size between the sixth
and eighth instead of the same size as the sixth. In *E. calidella* the anterior
dorso-median seta of the first eight abdominal segments is only about a fourth
instead of about half as long as the posterior dorso-median seta.

† Only the full-grown larvae of *Ephestia kuehniella* and *Ephestia elutella* may
be satisfactorily distinguished on the structural difference given here.

Head with less than six ocelli on each side. Eighth abdominal segment with nearest long seta above the spiracle 12
12. Head with four ocelli on each side. Labium without a pit or ring. (If a living larva is rolled between the thumb and forefinger it nearly always exudes a drop of brown liquid from its mouth.)......................
...........................**Hofmannophila pseudospretella** Stainton
Head with only two ocelli on each side. Labium (fig. 123) with a large pit or sclerotised ring. (If a living larva is rolled between the thumb and forefinger it exudes a nearly colourless liquid from the mouth.)
.....................................**Endrosis sarcitrella** Linnaeus
13. Head with six distinct ocelli on each side ....**Nemapogon granella** Linnaeus
Head with less than six ocelli on each side........................14
14. Head without distinct ocelli. Spiracle of seventh abdominal segment approximately as large as that of eighth segment ....
......................................**Tineola bisselliella** Hummel
Head with one or two distinct ocelli on each side. Spiracle of seventh abdominal segment distinctly smaller than that of eighth segment 15
15. Head nearly always with two distinct ocelli on each side ....
...............................**Haplotinea ditella** Pierce & Metcalfe
Head with a single ocellus on each side............................16
16. Abdomen with the first two setae below the spiracles of the first seven segments in a nearly vertical line with the most dorsal seta almost directly behind the spiracle (fig. 122) 17
Abdomen with the first two setae below the spiracles of the first seven segments in a more or less horizontal line and both considerably below the spiracle (as in fig. 121) 18
17. Antenna with first segment at least as long as second ....
.................................**Trichophaga tapetzella** Linnaeus
Antenna with first segment much shorter than second ....
......................................**Monopis rusticella** Clerck
18. Larva in a portable fusiform case which is dorso-ventrally flattened and has an opening flap at both ends............**Tinea pellionella** Linnaeus
Larva usually without a case; if in a case, the latter is round in cross-section and is completely sealed at one end 19
19. Abdominal prolegs of segments three to six each with 21–26 crochets ....
.....................................**Tinea pallescentella** Stainton
Abdominal prolegs of segments three to six each with 30 or more crochets
..................................**Niditinea fuscipunctella** Haworth

HYMENOPTERA*

This large Order contains the ants, bees and wasps, sawflies and a series of parasitic groups. About 100,000 species have been described, certain of which have highly developed social habits. They have two pairs of membranous wings, though a number, e.g. worker ants and some parasitic wasps, have none. The mouth-

* The British Bethylidae, including the warehouse species, have been keyed by Richards, O. W., 1939, *Trans R. ent. Soc. Lond.*, **89**, 297–299, and the Ichneumonidae associated with stored products by Richards, O. W., 1949, *Proc. R. ent. Soc. Lond. (B)*, **18**, 19–35.

parts are adapted for biting, in many they are also capable of lapping, and in some groups, e.g. bees, of sucking. In most species the first segment of the abdomen is fused to the metathorax and the second is constricted and forms a narrow waist, but in some primitive forms the abdomen is broadly sessile and the first segment is only partly amalgamated with the thorax. An ovipositor is always present in the females, and is modified for sawing, piercing, or stinging. Metamorphosis is complete. The larvae of those found associated with stored food (i.e. parasitic wasps) are white, legless, grub-like creatures frequently with a poorly developed head: they are usually internal parasites of immature stages of beetles and moths and consequently rarely seen.

The adults of the more common parasites of stored food insects

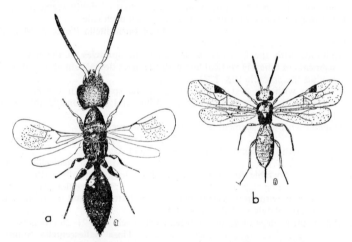

Fig. 124.—(*a*) *Holepyris hawaiiensis* Ashmead, a parasite of *Plodia* and *Ephestia*. Female. ×9. (*b*) *Bracon hebetor* Say, a parasite of *Ephestia*, *Corcyra*, *Sitotroga*, etc. Female. ×7. (After Richards and Herford)

are sometimes rather abundant on the windows of warehouses and granaries, where they are attracted to the light. Being parasitic, they may give an indication of an infestation by their particular hosts. Many of these parasites are very small, often about 1 mm. long. Two common species, *Holepyris hawaiiensis* Ashmead (Bethylidae) and *Bracon hebetor* Say (Braconidae), are illustrated in fig. 124.

DIPTERA

The Diptera (two-winged or true flies) are one of the most highly specialised Orders of insects, about 85,000 species having been described. They are easily recognised by having only a single pair of membranous wings, the hind pair being modified to form small club-shaped balancing organs known as halteres, The mouth-parts are modified for sucking or sucking and piercing, and mandibles are generally absent. Metamorphosis is complete.

The larvae or maggots never have true legs but sometimes have fleshy pseudopods. A well-developed head with horizontally biting mouth-parts is present only in the more primitive forms (Nematocera). Most have vertically biting mandibles and a posteriorly incomplete head which can be withdrawn into the thorax, or a vestigal head with the mandibles and maxillae fused to form mouth-hooks.

A number of flies such as house-flies and mosquitoes commonly enter warehouses and granaries either accidentally or in search of suitable places for hibernating. Only a few species regularly live in

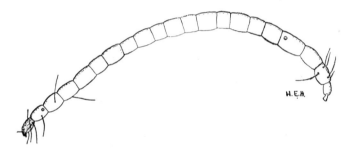

FIG. 125.—Larva of *Scenopinus fenestralis* Linnaeus.   ×4

stored food products. Among the latter are the cheese skipper (*Piophila casei* Linnaeus) and several species of *Drosophila*. The species of *Drosophila* or "vinegar fly" may become very numerous on materials that have been allowed to decay.

One species, the window fly (*Scenopinus fenestralis* Linnaeus), is commonly associated with grain in this country. The window fly is small (3–6 mm. long), the thorax is clothed with greyish yellow hairs, the abdomen is dark and flat, and the legs are greyish with brown femora. The larvae (fig. 125) are yellowish white, very narrow, active creatures about 20 mm. long when full grown. The fact that many of the abdominal segments are subdivided so that there appear to be 17 abdominal segments will serve to distinguish these larvae from those of all other insects found in similar situations. They prey on the larvae and pupae of beetles and moths.

SIPHONAPTERA

Fleas form a well-defined order of about 1,900 species of small, laterally compressed, wingless insects whose chief method of progression is by leaping. Their mouth-parts are modified for piercing and sucking, and all are blood-sucking ectoparasites of mammals and birds. They have a complete metamorphosis. The larvae are very active, narrow, maggot-like, legless creatures with biting mouth-parts. They live in the dust and refuse along walls or

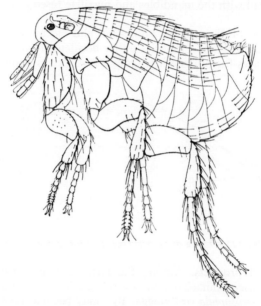

FIG. 126.—*Xenopsylla cheopis* Rothschild, the plague flea.   ×30

in the crevices between floor boards, and feed on almost any kind of organic matter.

A few species, e.g. the human flea (*Pulex irritans* Linnaeus) and those found on domestic animals and birds (*Leptopsylla, Xenopsylla* (fig. 126), *Ceratophyllus, Ctenocephalides* etc.) are sometimes found in granaries and warehouses.

INDEX

Names of Families and higher categories are in capitals and synonyms
in italics

Acheta, 4, 5
advena (Ahasverus), 12, 15, 22
Ahasverus, 12, 15, 22
Alphitobius, 38
Alphitophagus, 38
americana (Periplaneta), 4
Amphibolus, 7
Anagasta, 45
analis (Exkorynetes), 32
annulipes (Euborellia), 4, 5
ANOBIIDAE, 19, 32
Anobium, 33, 34
ANTHICIDAE, 9
Anthicus, 9, 12
anthracinus (Lathridius), 26
Anthrenus, 17, 26, 27, 29, 30
ANTHRIBIDAE, 12
APHANIPTERA, see SIPHON-
APTERA
arachidis (Marava), 4, 5
Araecerus, 12
Aridius, 26
Arrostelus, 6
ater (Dermestes), 19, 29, 30
Attagenus, 19, 29, 30
auricularia (Forficula), 4, 5
australasiae (Periplaneta), 4

bergrothi (Thes), 24, 25
BETHYLIDAE, 55
biannulipes (Peregrinator), 7
bifasciatus (Alphitophagus), 38
bisselliella (Tineola), 48, 49, 55
Blaps, 13, 37
Blatella, 4

Blatta, 4
BOSTRICHIDAE, 15
Bracon, 56
BRACONIDAE, 55
BRUCHIDAE, 13
Bruchus, 12, 13
brunneus (Lyctus), 16, 17
buqueti (Thaneroclerus), 16, 31

Cadra, 45
Caenocorse, 40
Calandra, 20
calidella (Ephestia), 47, 51, 54
californicus (Henoticus), 14
Callosobruchus, 13
campestris (Lyctocoris), 7
CARABIDAE, 8, 10, 13
Carcinops, 10, 11
carnivorus (Dermestes), 28, 29
Carpophilus, 21, 22
Cartodere, 26
carus (Paratillus), 31
Caryedon, 11, 13
casei (Piophila), 57
castaneum (Tribolium), 18, 41
Cathartus, 22
Caulophilus, 20
cautella (Ephestia), 45, 46, 47, 48,
49, 50, 53, 54
cellaris (Cryptophagus), 12
cephalonica (Corcyra), 43, 45, 46,
47, 52, 54
Ceratophyllus, 58
cerealella (Sitotroga), 44, 46, 48, 51
cheopis (Xenopsylla), 58

clavipes (Ptinus), 35, 37
CLERIDAE, 13, 16, 30
COLEOPTERA, 8
confine (Euophryum), 18, 20
confusum (Tribolium), 39, 41
constrictus (Cartodere), 26
Corcyra, 43, 45, 46, 47, 52, 54, 56
cornutus (Gnathocerus), 38, 41
Corticaria, 24, 25
costalis (Hypsopygia), 44, 45, 46, 54
crocicapitella (Monopis), 48, 49
Cryptolestes, 13, 14, 21
CRYPTOPHAGIDAE, 14, 15
Cryptophagus, 12, 15
Ctenocephalides, 58
CUCUJIDAE, 14, 21
CURCULIONIDAE, 9, 19
Cydia, 54

DERMAPTERA, 4
Dermestes, 17, 18, 19, 27, 28, 29, 30
DERMESTIDAE, 17, 18, 19, 27
destructor (Tribolium), 39, 41
diaperinus (Alphitobius), 38
DICTYOPTERA, 3
"dimidiatus Group" (Carpophilus), 22
DIPTERA, 55
ditella (Haplotinea), 48, 50, 51, 55
domestica (Thermobia), 2
domesticum (Anobium), 33
domesticus (Acheta), 4
dominica (Rhizopertha), 15
Drosophila, 57

elutella (Ephestia), 44, 46, 47, 48, 49, 50, 52, 53, 54
ENDOMYCHIDAE, 14
Endrosis, 43, 48, 53, 55
Ephestia, 7, 44, 45, 46, 47, 48, 49, 50, 51, 52, 53, 54, 56
Euborellia, 4, 5
Euophryum, 18, 20
Exkorynetes, 32

farinalis (Pyralis), 44, 46, 54
fasciculatus (Araecerus), 12
fenestralis (Scenopinus), 57
ferrugineum (Tribolium), 41
filiformis (Microgramme), 24, 26
filum (Microgramme), 26
flavipes (Xylocoris), 7
floralis (Anthicus), 12
Forficula, 4, 5
frischii (Dermestes), 27, 28, 29
fumata (Typhaea), 27
fur (Ptinus), 37
fuscipunctella (Niditinea), 50, 51, 55

GELECHIIDAE, 43
germanica (Blatella), 4
globulus (Trigonogenius), 37
Gnathocerus, 38, 41
granaria (*Calandra*), 20
granaria (Oligota), 13
granarium (Trogoderma), 30
granarius (Sitophilus), 8, 20
granella (Nemapogon), 48, 50, 55
gularis (Paralipsa), 41, 45, 46, 47, 52, 53

haemorrhoidalis (Dermestes), 19, 30
Haplotinea, 48, 50, 51, 55
Harpalus, 10
hawaiiensis (Holepyris), 56
hebetor (Bracon), 56
HEMIPTERA, 6
hemipterus (Carpophilus), 21
Henoticus, 14
hilleri (Eurostus), 35, 36
hirta (Mycetaea), 14
hirtellus (Ptinus), 35, 37
HISTERIDAE, 11
Hofmannophila, 48, 49, 53, 55
Holepyris, 56
hololeucus (Niptus), 36, 37
huttoni (Pentarthrum), 20
HYMENOPTERA, 55
Hypsopygia, 44, 45, 46, 54

inclusum (Trogoderma), 26, 30
insectella (Haplotinea), 51
interpunctella (Plodia), 45, 46, 47, 48, 49, 50, 54
irritans (Pulex), 58

khapra (Trogoderma), 30
kuehniella (Ephestia), 45, 46, 47, 48, 49, 50, 53, 54

Laemophloeinae, 14, 21
laevigatus (Alphitobius), 38
lardarius (Dermestes), 18, 28, 29
Lasioderma, 31, 33
Laspeyresia, 53, 54
Latheticus, 39, 40
LATHRIDIIDAE, 18, 23
Lathridius, 23, 26
latinasus (Caulophilus), 20
LEPIDOPTERA, 42
Lepisma, 2
Leptophloeus, 14
Leptopsylla, 58
ligneus (Carpophilus), 22
Lophocateres, 17, 18
LOPHOCATERIDAE, 18
Lyctinae, 17
Lyctocoris, 7
Lyctus, 16, 17

maculatus (Dermestes), 27, 28
Marava, 4, 5
mauritanicus (Tenebroides), 13, 18
maxillosus (Gnathocerus), 38, 41
megatoma (Attagenus), 30
mercator (Oryzaephilus), 22, 23
Microgramme, 24, 26
"minutus Group" (Lathridius), 26
molitor (Tenebrio), 38
Monopis, 48, 49, 50, 53, 55
Monotoma, 12
mucronata (Blaps), 13, 37
Mycetaea, 14
MYCETOPHAGIDAE, 19, 26
Mycetophagus, 19, 25, 27

navale (Tribolium), 41
Necrobia, 31, 32
Nemapogon, 48, 50, 55
Niditinea, 50, 51, 55
Niptus, 36, 37
NITIDULIDAE, 12, 21
nodifer (Aridius), 25

obscurus (Tenebrio), 39
obsoletus (Carpophilus), 21
OECOPHORIDAE, 43
Oligota, 13
orientalis (Blatta), 4
ORTHOPTERA, 4
oryzae (Caulophilus), 20
oryzae (Latheticus), 40
oryzae (Sitophilus), 20
Oryzaephilus, 7, 14, 22
ovatus (Alphitobius), 39

pallescentella (Tinea), 43, 48, 51, 55
Palorus, 40
panicea (Sitodrepa), 33
paniceum (Stegobium), 33, 34
Paralipsa, 42, 45, 46, 47, 52
Paratillus, 32
pellio (Attagenus), 19, 29, 30
pellionella (Tinea), 44, 48, 50, 51, 52, 53, 55
Pentarthrum, 20
Peregrinator, 7
Periplaneta, 4
personatus (Reduvius), 7
peruvianus (Dermestes), 19, 30
PHYCITINAE, 54
piceus Auct. (Alphitobius), 39
piceus Oliv. (Alphitobius), 39
piceus (Attagenus), 30
Piezostethus, 7
Piophila, 57
Planolestes, 14
Plodia, 7, 45, 46, 47, 48, 49, 54, 56
pomonella (Laspeyresia), 53, 54
Pseudeurostus, 35, 36
pseudominutus (Lathridius), 23, 26
pseudospretella (Hofmannophila), 48, 49, 53, 55

PSOCOPTERA, 5
PTINIDAE, 15, 34
Ptinus, 35, 36
pubescens (Corticaria), 24, 25
Pulex, 58
pumilio (Carcinops), 10, 11
punctatum (Anobium), 33, 34
punctulata (Corticaria), 25
pusillus (Lophocateres), 17, 18
pusillus (Ptinus), 35, 37
PYRALIDAE, 43, 44, 45
PYRALINAE, 54
Pyralis, 44, 46, 54

quadriguttatus (Mycetophagus), 25
27

ratzeburgii (Palorus), 40
Reduvius, 7
Rhizopertha, 15
RHIZOPHAGIDAE, 12
ruficollis (Necrobia), 31
rufipes (Harpalus), 10
rufipes (Necrobia), 31, 32
rusticella (Monopis), 50, 53, 55

saccharina (Lepisma), 2
sarcitrella (Endrosis), 43, 48, 53, 55
Scenopinus, 57
scrophulariae (Anthrenus), 26
serratus (Caryedon), 11
serricorne (Lasioderma), 31, 33
SILVANIDAE, 14, 22
Silvanus, 23
SIPHONAPTERA, 56
Sitodrepa, 34
Sitophilus, 8, 20
Sitotroga, 44, 46, 48, 52, 56
STAPHYLINIDAE, 9
Stegobium, 33, 34

stercorea (Typhaea), 25, 27
striatum (Anobium), 33
subdepressus (Palorus), 40
surinamensis (Oryzaephilus), 22, 23

tapetzella (Trichophaga), 48, 49, 55
Tarsostenus, 31
tectus (Ptinus), 35, 36
Tenebrio, 13, 38, 39
TENEBRIONIDAE, 13, 18, 37
Tenebroides, 13, 18
Thaneroclerus, 16, 31
Thermobia, 2
Thes, 24, 25
THYSANURA, 2
Tinea, 43, 44, 48, 50, 51, 52, 53, 55
TINEIDAE, 43, 45
Tineola, 48, 50, 55
Tipnus, 36, 37
TORTRICIDAE, 43
Tribolium, 7, 17, 18, 39, 41
Trichophaga, 48, 49, 55
Trigonogenius, 37
Trogoderma, 26, 30
TROGOSITIDAE, 18
Typhaea, 19, 25, 27

unicolor (Tipnus), 36, 37
univittatus (Tarsostenus), 31

venator (Amphibolus), 7
verbasci (Anthrenus), 29
violacea (Necrobia), 31
vulpinus (Dermestes), 27

Xenopsylla, 58
Xylocoris, 7

zeamais (Sitophilus), 20